PRENTICE-HALL FOUNDATIONS OF PHILOSOPHY SERIES

Virgil Aldrich	PHILOSOPHY OF ART
William Alston	PHILOSOPHY OF LANGUAGE
Stephen Barker	PHILOSOPHY OF MATHEMATICS
Roderick Chisholm	THEORY OF KNOWLEDGE
William Dray	PHILOSOPHY OF HISTORY
William Frankena	ETHICS
Carl Hempel	PHILOSOPHY OF NATURAL SCIENCE
John Hick	PHILOSOPHY OF RELIGION
Sidney Hook	POLITICAL PHILOSOPHY
John Lenz	PHILOSOPHY OF EDUCATION
Richard Rudner	PHILOSOPHY OF SOCIAL SCIENCE
Wesley Salmon	LOGIC
Richard Taylor	METAPHYSICS

Elizabeth and Monroe Beardsley, editors

Philosophy of Mathematics

PHILOSOPHY

OF

MATHEMATICS

FOUNDATIONS OF PHILOSOPHY SERIES

Stephen F. *Francis* Barker

The Ohio State University

PRENTICE-HALL, INC.   ENGLEWOOD CLIFFS, N. J.

PHILOSOPHY OF MATHEMATICS, Barker

FOUNDATIONS OF PHILOSOPHY SERIES

C-66380

Current printing (last digit):

12   11   10   9   8   7   6   5   4   3

QA
9
.B26

PRENTICE-HALL INTERNATIONAL, INC., London

PRENTICE-HALL OF AUSTRALIA, PTY., LTD., Sydney

PRENTICE-HALL OF CANADA, LTD., Toronto

PRENTICE-HALL OF INDIA (PRIVATE) LTD., New Delhi

PRENTICE-HALL OF JAPAN, INC., Tokyo

PRENTICE-HALL DE MEXICO, S.A., Mexico City

Reasoning upon its own dark fiction,
In doubt which is self-contradiction.
—Blake

FOUNDATIONS

OF PHILOSOPHY

Many of the problems of philosophy are of such broad relevance to human concerns, and so complex in their ramifications, that they are, in one form or another, perennially present. Though in the course of time they yield in part to philosophical inquiry, they may need to be rethought by each age in the light of its broader scientific knowledge and deepened ethical and religious experience. Better solutions are found by more refined and rigorous methods. Thus, one who approaches the study of philosophy in the hope of understanding the best of what it affords will look for both fundamental issues and contemporary achievements.

Written by a group of distinguished philosophers, the Foundations of Philosophy Series aims to exhibit some of the main problems in the various fields of philosophy as they stand at the present stage of philosophical history.

While certain fields are likely to be represented in most introductory courses in philosophy, college classes differ widely in emphasis, in method of instruction, and in rate of progress. Every instructor needs freedom to change his course as his own philosophical interests, the size and makeup of his classes, and the needs of his students vary from year to year. The thirteen volumes in the Foundations of Philosophy Series—each complete in itself, but complementing the others—offer a new flexibility to the instructor, who can create his own textbook by combining several volumes as he wishes, and can choose different combinations at different times. Those volumes that are not used in an introductory course will be found valuable, along with other texts or collections of readings, for the more specialized upper-level courses.

ELIZABETH BEARDSLEY   MONROE BEARDSLEY

PREFACE

Among the ancients, mathematics provided copious food for philosophical reflection, and in recent times it has again done so and with a vengeance. The philosophy of mathematics is at present a difficult and controversial branch of philosophy. With successive hammer blows, new and profound technical results have struck down old preconceptions, effecting what later times are likely to look back upon as one of the important intellectual upheavals in the history of thought. But it is too early for us to feel confident that the philosophical significance of these technical results has been properly understood. One thing is clear: philosophical discussion of mathematics cannot profitably be carried on in total ignorance of modern technical developments. This book therefore tries to strike a compromise: it aims to offer some informal discussion of results in mathematics and mathematical logic, and it aims also to present some philosophical reasoning about them. Problems connected with geometry and problems connected with number are considered separately, not because this is a fair way of dividing up modern mathematics—it is not—but because philosophers' problems about mathematics have tended to fall under these two headings.

Philosophers of recent decades have written frequently about mathematics, and in some of their popular expositions certain misleading oversimplifications have become rather deeply entrenched. Thus, it is often asserted that the theorems of mathematics have to be analytic simply because they follow deductively from their axioms; it is often asserted that the axioms of an abstract system define its primitive terms; it is often asserted that the development of non-Euclidean geometry is what decisively shows Kant's philosophy of space to have been mistaken; and it is often asserted that mathematical truth and mathematical existence amount to nothing more than deducibility from the axioms. All these assertions are misleading oversimplifications that I have tried to avoid. If readers find that I am guilty of replacing them by other misleading oversimplifications of my own, then I can at least reply that it sometimes is progress in philosophy to pass from old crudities to new ones.

To my wife, Dr. Evelyn Masi Barker, I owe a debt of gratitude for her encouragement and her help with the manuscript.

STEPHEN F. BARKER

CONTENTS

Philosophy of Mathematics

INTRODUCTION

1

Ever since philosophy began among the ancient Greeks, mathematics has been one of the great sources of philosophical problems. For the Greeks, mathematics was pre-eminently geometry; and if one studies geometry in the traditional manner, a host of philosophical questions comes flooding in right from the very beginning. Euclid defines a point as "that which has no parts": but how is this to be understood? Isn't it impossible for there to be anything without parts? And if there were any such things, could we ever see them or know anything about them? People often have regarded Euclidean geometry as descriptive of the physical world; but it seems difficult to believe that the world can be built of points, for if points have no extension, then even infinitely many points are not enough to make up a volume of space. Are points then just ideas in our minds? Are they fictions with which we delude ourselves? Or are they real things but of an unobservable kind? In either case, why is it that the principles of geometry can be applied to the world by architects and engineers? Here are several connected problems: the problem of what sort of meaning geometrical terms have; the problem of whether the principles of geometry can be true; the problem of how, if at all, we can attain knowledge in the field of geometry; the problem of why geometry applies to the observable world.

The rise of non-Euclidean geometries poured new fuel on these flames. If geometries are mathematically legitimate that contain laws logically incompatible with the laws of Euclidean geometry, what has become of the notion of mathematical truth? When one law is incompatible with another, they cannot both be true. Are mathematicians no

1

longer concerned with truth? It is hard to see how the study of geometry can have any significance unless it involves pursuit of the truth about space.

Concerning the mathematics of number, a variety of similar questions arise, having to do with the meanings of the terms used, the possibility of attaining truth, and, in fact, whether truth is even sought in this part of mathematics; there are questions about what kind of knowledge, if any, is involved, and questions as to why the laws of number apply to reality. In connection with the mathematics of number, a further and somewhat different problem also arises, the problem of mathematical existence. Now, the principles of geometry can all be understood as hypothetical principles which do not assert the existence of anything: "If there is a figure which is a triangle, then the sum of its angles is equal to two right angles." We need not think of geometry as including any such laws as "There exists a triangle." In the mathematics of number, on the other hand, there are many laws that do seem to assert the existence of things; for example, "There exists exactly one number y such that x times y equals x, whatever number x may be." This sort of law definitely seems to assert the existence of something (the number 1), so the law cannot easily be understood in a hypothetical sense, as the geometrical laws can be. But what sort of existence is involved? With what sort of reality does this part of mathematics deal? Is the existence statement to be understood in some fairly literal sense, or must it be understood quite figuratively?

These are philosophical problems, for they have to do with very general, basic questions about meaning, truth, reality, and knowledge. Practicing mathematicians, concerned with extending their subject, usually give but cursory attention to such problems about its foundations. Someone may say, "Yes, and that's to the credit of mathematicians. For these supposed 'problems' are confused pseudo-problems. This sort of philosophical speculation about mathematics is meaningless." Such a remark is too crude, however. Perhaps most of the perplexities that philosophers have felt regarding mathematics do arise out of misunderstandings of one sort or another; but all the same, the problems here are serious intellectual matters, for the misunderstandings out of which they arise are important and persuasive ones, not silly ones easily rooted out. These problems deserve to be examined and unravelled, not just dismissed out of hand. The person who cuts the Gordian knot instead of unravelling it is pretty sure to be entangled by it himself before long.

Here we may compare the philosophy of mathematics with the philosophy of religion. After careful reflection upon what has been said about the Deity by religionists and by philosophers down through the ages, one possible conclusion that we might come to is that religious talk is basically confused and incoherent, and in the end makes little sense. Even if this negative conclusion were to be reached, however, that would not mean that philosophical problems about religion do not deserve attention; far from it. For if religious thought is confused, then at any rate its confusions reflect strong and deep human intellectual tendencies; and these tendencies toward confusion can hardly be outgrown unless their sources are traced and understood.[1] The same can be said of the philosophy of mathematics.

A priori and empirical knowledge   Before we directly discuss any of the special problems of the philosophy of mathematics, let us first consider some distinctions that have been important to philosophers and that have underlain much discussion in the philosophy of mathematics. The first of these is a distinction to which philosophers have long given attention, that between what they have called a priori knowledge and what they have called empirical (or a posteriori) knowledge. Traditionally, rationalists were philosophers who held a priori knowledge to be far more important than empirical knowledge, while empiricists were philosophers who took the opposite view. One question that has been regarded as fundamental in the philosophy of mathematics is the question whether mathematical knowledge is a priori or empirical (assuming that knowledge is indeed attainable in the field of mathematics). The nature of this distinction between two kinds of knowledge has not always been explained very clearly, however. The term "empirical" means "based on experience," and "a priori" means "attainable prior to experience"; but how are these phrases to be understood?

Sometimes philosophers of the past have allowed the distinction between a priori and empirical knowledge to become entangled with a supposed distinction between a priori concepts and empirical concepts, and have thought that knowledge involving empirical concepts must be empirical knowledge and that knowledge involving a priori concepts must be a priori knowledge. Empirical concepts were held to be ideas that have been 'abstracted' by the mind from what is 'given' in sense experience, while a priori concepts were held to be ideas not acquired by the mind in that manner. There are two defects in this approach, however. First, even if the distinction between a priori and empirical concepts made good sense, still there surely could be empirical knowledge not wholly expressible in empirical concepts and a priori knowledge not wholly expressible in a priori concepts. But second, and more important, this distinction between empirical and a priori concepts does

---

[1] For a discussion of the coherency of religious thought, see Chaps. 6 and 7 in John Hick, *Philosophy of Religion*, Prentice-Hall Foundations of Philosophy Series.

not make good sense. It rests upon a crude and outdated psychological theory about 'abstraction'—a quasi-mechanical process which the mind supposedly can perform upon what is 'given' in experience. The theory provides no clue as to how it could be determined which concepts can and which cannot be 'abstracted' from what is 'given' in sense experience. Philosophers did commonly agree that when a person sees a red thing his mind can 'abstract' the 'given' idea of redness, and that when he sees a virtuous thing his mind cannot abstract from it the idea of virtue; but they gave no coherent explanation of why one need say that the cases differ in this way. The distinction between a priori and empirical knowledge has been much obscured by this overlay of outdated psychology. Let us try to formulate the distinction in a more useful manner.

Suppose someone knows that ravens are black, that Caesar was born before Caligula, that hydrogen molecules always consist of two atoms, or that there will be a gale tomorrow. These are clear-cut examples of what philosophers have meant by *empirical* knowledge. Each of these pieces of knowledge is based on experience in this sense: to know any one of these facts a person must not only understand what is meant but must also possess evidence drawn from sense experience— that is, evidence regarding what has been seen or heard or felt or smelled or tasted. In order to know that ravens are black, I must not only understand what this means, I must also have seen ravens, or seen feathers that they have left behind, or heard reports of observers who have seen such things, or something of the sort. Of course, even without evidence, a person could *believe* that ravens are black, that Caesar was born before Caligula, that hydrogen molecules contain two atoms, or that there will be a gale tomorrow. But belief, even if true, is not knowledge when it lacks justification. The point is that only sensory observations can provide the kind of justification needed to entitle a person to say that he *knows* facts like these. If I do not have any sort of observational evidence relative to ravens, then it is certainly false to say that I know them to be black. To claim to know this kind of thing without knowing it on the basis of evidence gained through sense experience would be self-contradictory. Summing up, we may define empirical knowledge as knowledge that requires justification from experience.

There are other examples of knowledge, however, which do not depend upon experience in this way. Suppose someone knows that ravens are birds, that Caesar either was born before Caligula or was not born before Caligula, that hydrogen molecules are molecules, or that there will be a storm tomorrow if there is a gale. These are clear-cut examples of what philosophers have meant by *a priori* knowledge. A person does not have to have observed ravens directly or indirectly in order to be entitled to say that he knows all ravens are birds; he does not have to have looked into Roman history in order to know that Caesar either was or was not born before Caligula; he need not have watched physicists' experiments with hydrogen in order to know that hydrogen molecules are molecules; nor need he have seen tomorrow's weather map to know that there will be a storm if there is a gale. In these cases the only experience that is required is whatever experience may be needed in order to enable him to understand the words in which the knowledge is expressed: no sense experience beyond this is necessary to justify his claim that he knows. Summing up, we may define a priori knowledge as knowledge that does not need to be justified by experience.

This distinction between a priori and empirical knowledge is of philosophical importance both because of the clarification it effects and because of the problems it raises. It helps us to see that subjects such as physics, biology, and history, all of which are primarily concerned with matters of empirical knowledge, must therefore rely upon observations in order to establish their conclusions. A subject like logic, in contrast, is concerned only with a priori knowledge (logic seeks a priori knowledge of the rules governing the validity of arguments) and therefore need not rely upon observations in reaching its conclusions. The question then arises, is mathematics like physics or is it like logic in this respect? Or is it partly like the one and partly like the other? And one very general philosophical problem that the distinction raises is the problem of how we attain a priori knowledge: is it through some special insight into reality, or through insight into our own minds, through understanding of language, or what? If mathematical knowledge is a priori, not justified by experience, then what is it based on?

Connected with this distinction between a priori and empirical knowledge is an important distinction between two types of reasoning, deduction and induction. We shall not try to define these fully, but let us notice how they differ. *Deduction* is reasoning in which we can know a priori that if no logical mistake has been made and if the premises are true, then the conclusion will have to be true also. An example is the reasoning: "Every even number is divisible by two; no prime number is divisible by two; therefore, no prime number is even." Here there is no logical mistake, and we can know a priori that if both premises are true then the conclusion will have to be true also. This is an example of the sort of knowledge with which logic deals, for in this example the deductive argument is valid by virtue of its *logical form*. That is, with regard to *any* argument of the form "Every $\#\#\#$ is $///$, no *** is $///$, therefore no *** is $\#\#\#$" one can know a priori that if the premises are true, then the conclusion has to be true too. In logic, the notion of logical form is understood as having to do solely with the arrangement of the words "every", "no", "is" and certain other 'logical' words including "some", "not", "and", "or", and "if".

The argument just considered is valid by virtue of its logical form—by virtue of the arrangement of these 'logical' words in it. However, to say this is not to give any philosophical explanation of why the reasoning is valid. It is not to say whence we obtain our priori knowledge that if the premises are true, then the conclusion will have to be true too. People who agree about what logical form the argument has can still disagree about whether our knowledge that arguments of this form are valid comes from insight into reality, into the mind, or into language. Nor is there any ground for imagining that *all* valid deductive reasoning is valid solely by virtue of its logical form. The argument "Mt. McKinley is higher than Pikes Peak, Pikes Peak is higher than Mt. Washington; therefore, Mt. McKinley is higher than Mt. Washington" expresses a perfectly valid piece of deductive reasoning, even though logic does not happen to recognize any such 'logical form' as "x is —er than y, y is —er than z; therefore x is —er than z." The limited group of words upon which logicians focus their attention has not happened to include "—er than," and this is regarded as a 'nonlogical' expression. But the reasoning is valid all the same, because we know a priori that if the premises of this argument are true, then the conclusion will be true too. To be sure, someone might object, saying that this argument is valid only if you add the premise: whenever a first thing is higher than a second, and the second higher than a third, then the first is higher than the third. However, there is no more need to add such a premise here than there is need in the preceding example to add the premise: whenever everything of one kind is of a second kind and nothing of a third kind is of the second kind, then nothing of the third kind is of the first kind. We need not add these additional premises, for in each case the stated premises alone are sufficient, in the sense that one can know a priori that if they are true, then the conclusion must be true. In each case, the suggested additional premise is not really a premise but rather is an expression of the rule of inference according to which the reasoning proceeds; that is, of the way in which the conclusion is got from the premise. The moral of this is that although logical form is important to deduction, it is not all-important.

In contrast with deduction, *induction* is reasoning in which a conclusion is inferred which expresses an empirical conjecture going beyond what the data say; and therefore we cannot know a priori that if the data are true, the conclusion will be true too. For example, suppose I have observed many ravens, all of which were black. Then I can reason inductively that probably, therefore, all ravens are black. But the truth of my data constitutes no a priori guarantee that the conclusion that all ravens are black must be true. At best, all that one can say is that the data support and confirm the conclusion, not that they absolutely guarantee its truth.

The distinction between deduction and induction is connected with the distinction between a priori and empirical knowledge in the following way. If we are giving a proof of an a priori statement, showing that it really is something that is known to be true, then there is no reason why our proof should not be deductive at every step. It should never be necessary to use inductive reasoning to establish a conclusion that embodies just a priori knowledge. But if we are establishing an empirical conclusion, then at least some of the steps in our reasoning must be inductive; an empirical conclusion could never be established by reasoning that was completely deductive at every step.[2]

Analytic and synthetic knowledge   In addition to the distinction between a priori and empirical knowledge, philosophers have also concerned themselves with another related distinction, that between analytic and synthetic knowledge. This distinction was introduced into philosophy by the eighteenth-century German philosopher Immanuel Kant, and has been a source of controversy ever since. In trying to explain his distinction between analytic and synthetic knowledge, Kant made use of the notion of judgment. In Kant's view, to know something, or even to have a belief of any kind, is to have made a judgment; the judgment may have been made consciously or unconsciously, and it may or may not be put into words and uttered as a statement. Kant pictured the mental act of making a judgment as an act of connecting concepts, holding them together in consciousness. According to this view, someone who knows that all bachelors are unmarried has connected together in his consciousness the concept of bachelor and the concept of being married (and has made this connection in a manner which logic calls universal and affirmative). Similarly, someone who knows that no pigs fly has connected together in his consciousness the concept of pig and the concept of flying (and has made this connection in a universal and negative manner).

Kant felt that a distinction has to be drawn between two basically different sorts of judgments. This distinction is parallel to the distinction in chemistry between *synthesis*—the act of putting together things that were uncombined and different—and *analysis*, the act of separating out of something a component that was present in it. Among judgments, there are on the one hand those in which the mind synthesizes or puts

---

[2] For fuller discussion of this point see Carl Hempel, *Philosophy of Natural Science*, Prentice-Hall Foundations of Philosophy Series.

together concepts in a manner that does not accord with any intrinsic relation they have to one another. The judgment that no pigs fly is an example of such a *synthetic* judgment, for there is presumably nothing about the concept of pig which intrinsically excludes flying. On the other hand, there are judgments in which the mind analyzes a concept, separating out another concept that is intrinsically part of it. The judgment that all bachelors are unmarried is an example of such an *analytic* judgment, for the concept of being unmarried is an intrinsic part of the concept of being a bachelor. Thus, we may give a first account of the distinction by saying, according to Kant's basic idea, the following: a judgment is analytic if, and only if, nothing but reflection upon the concepts in the judgment and upon the form of combination of these concepts is needed to enable one to know whether the judgment is true. A judgment is synthetic if, and only if, mere reflection upon the concepts in the judgment and upon their form of combination is not sufficient to enable one to know whether the judgment is true; to know that, appeal to something further is required.

Many present-day philosophers do not care for Kant's talk about 'judgments' and 'concepts,' considered as mental phenomena. However, we can rephrase this first account of the distinction between the analytic and the synthetic in a way more acceptable to them. Let us say that a *statement* is analytic if, and only if, nothing other than understanding it is necessary in order to enable one to know whether it is true. A statement is synthetic if understanding it never is sufficient to enable one to know whether it is true. By talking about statements instead of judgments and concepts we can avoid some unnecessary disputes over Kantian psychology.

Kant also gives a second account of the distinction between the analytic and synthetic, an account which he felt amounted to the same thing as the first account, but which is put differently. According to this second account, the paradigm examples of analytic truths are logical truths. Consider the statement that all dogs are dogs, and the statement that if some dogs are intelligent creatures then some intelligent creatures are dogs. These two statements are true, and indeed all statements of the form "All so-and-so's are so-and-so's" and of the form "If some so-and-so's are such-and-such's then some such-and-such's are so-and-so's" are equally true. Statements like these are true merely because of the way such logical words as "all," "some," and "if" are arranged in them; hence they are said to be true by virtue of their logical form and are called logical truths. Kant's idea was that all statements (he would have said judgments) whose truth just depends on their logical form are analytic, and that it is these statements which are the basic sort of analytically true statements.

Moreover, a statement (or judgment) which is not obviously analytic may be analytic in a hidden way. Suppose we can demonstrate that a given statement is logically equivalent to one which is clearly analytic; then the given statement must be analytic too, provided our demonstration employs only clearly analytic principles. Here is a way of *showing* that a given statement is analytic, even though this analyticity was perhaps not obvious at first. For example, suppose someone says that all oculists are eye-doctors. His statement may be regarded as having the logical form "All so-and-so's are such-and-such's," a logical form not all examples of which are true; therefore, the statement does not seem to be true merely by virtue of its logical form. Suppose, however, that the statement is made because of the speaker's intention to use the word "oculist" to mean the same as the term "eye-doctor." The speaker, consciously or unconsciously, is employing the definition: "By 'oculist' I mean 'eye-doctor.'" In the light of this definition, we are entitled to say that his original statement that oculists are eye-doctors really is equivalent to saying that all eye-doctors are eye-doctors. This latter statement is true merely by virtue of its logical form. Therefore, we may say that the original statement is analytic, not because it is explicitly in the form of a logical truth, but because it admits of being translated into one merely by appeal to a definition.

Thus, according to this second account, a true statement is analytic if and only if it is true by virtue of its logical form, or if, through appeal to definitions, it can be translated into a statement true by virtue of its logical form. A false statement would be analytic if and only if it is false by virtue of its logical form, or if, through appeal to definitions, it could be translated into a statement false by virtue of its logical form. And of course a statement is synthetic if and only if it is not analytic. Kant felt that this second account of the distinction was equivalent to the first account; and many subsequent philosophers have tended to agree with him.

Kant felt that analytic knowledge (that is, knowledge expressible in analytic statements, or judgments) poses no worrisome problems for philosophy. Kant thought it obvious how the mind is able to attain analytic knowledge, all of which is of course a priori knowledge. In knowing, for instance, that all bachelors are unmarried, a person possesses a piece of knowledge that merely reflects the nature of his own concepts, or as we might prefer to say, reflects the way he understands his own language. In order to know this, the person need only detect that the second concept is a component of the first; he need not possess information about the world outside his own mind, or even about the hidden aspects of his own mind itself. Everything is obvious, Kant felt; employing the concept of bachelor that we do employ, simple consistency is our justification for maintaining that whoever falls under the concept of bachelor falls also under the concept of being unmarried. This is something that we can know with perfect certainty and clarity; its only drawback is that it is something so empty and trivial that it barely seems to deserve to be called a piece of knowledge.

Synthetic knowledge, on the other hand, seemed to Kant to pose problems for the philosopher. Synthetic judgments have the advantage of being neither empty nor trivial; by linking together concepts that are not intrinsically related, they express important conjectures about the world. But how can we know that they are true? Mere consistency alone is not enough to entitle me to link together concepts in a synthetic judgment; there must be something else, a *tertium quid* (a third thing, in addition to the minimum of two concepts) which entitles me to synthesize the separate concepts of a synthetic judgment. With regard to synthetic judgments that are empirical, Kant was satisfied with the answer that sense experience constitutes the 'third thing' that can justify my judging, say, that no pigs fly. I have seen pigs and have observed how they differ in design and behavior from birds and blimps, and this sense experience is the 'third thing' on the basis of which I can be entitled to make the judgment.

But what about synthetic a priori judgments? Here the deep philosophical problem seemed to Kant to arise. Suppose there is some knowledge that is both a priori (that is, not justified by sense experience) and synthetic (not justified merely by the intrinsic connections of the concepts involved—or if you prefer, not justified by the ways the terms are understood). Such synthetic a priori knowledge would have to be justified by some very remarkable 'third thing.' If there is such synthetic a priori knowledge, it would be a matter of great importance to understand how we do attain it. Kant felt that mathematics provided the very clearest instances of such synthetic a priori knowledge.

The open texture of language   We have been discussing the distinction between a priori and empirical knowledge and the distinction between analytic and synthetic knowledge, and we have spoken of both these distinctions as if they were sharp and precise. However, although the distinctions are philosophically important, we must notice that they are not absolutely precise. There are borderline cases which do not definitely belong either to the a priori or to the empirical category, and borderline cases which do not definitely belong either to the analytic category or to the synthetic category. Indeed, sometimes the most interesting cases are ones that fall on or near the borderlines.

A simple case of this borderline sort is the case of someone who knows that all spiders have eight legs. Is his knowledge empirical and necessarily based on experience, or is it a priori, not requiring justification gleaned from observations of spiders? (Equally, we may ask, is it analytic or is it synthetic?) Before being entitled to say we know that they always have eight legs do we or don't we need to look at as many as we can of the spiders of the world? "Well," someone may say impatiently, "it all depends on how you are using the word 'spider.' If having eight legs is part of your definition of a spider, then it's a priori and analytic that all spiders have eight legs; and if not, then it's empirical and synthetic." In a way this is quite right. We must distinguish between the *sentence* (the series of words) "Spiders have eight legs" and the various different *statements* that someone could make by uttering that sentence. Someone who uttered this sentence and was using the word "spider" in such a way that having eight legs was part of his definition of the word would be making an a priori and analytic statement. And someone who uttered that same sentence using the word "spider" in such a way that having eight legs was not part of his definition of the word would be making an empirical and synthetic statement. This is not the whole story, however. What about someone who utters the sentence without first defining the word, someone who is using the word just in its everyday way? Has he made an a priori and analytic or an empirical and synthetic statement? Suppose an expedition comes back from the headwaters of the Amazon bearing specimens of a hitherto unsuspected species of creatures, black and hairy, with the looks and habits of the tarantula, but having only six legs: using the word "spider" in the ordinary way, how should we describe this find? Should we say, "Here, surprisingly enough, is a six-legged spider"; or should we say, "Here is a creature very like a spider, but it isn't a spider because it hasn't eight legs"? There is no definite answer to this question, for the everyday use of the word "spider" is not sharp in this respect. It is not precisely settled in ordinary language whether or not it would be self-contradictory to speak of spiders with six legs. All we can say is that in the light of our past use of the term, we would be justified in feeling some tendency to say the first thing, but also we would be justified in feeling some tendency to say the second thing. Here, then, is an example of a case in which a piece of knowledge is on the borderline between a priori and empirical, and also on the borderline between analytic and synthetic; it does not fit definitely into our categories. In this sense, our ordinary use of the term "spider" displays what some recent philosophers would call an 'openness of texture'. Our tendencies concerning the use of the word form a loosely knit pattern which does not definitely provide for all possibilities.

Let us consider one further example, more important in nature. Before the time of Copernicus the term "motion" and the words and phrases correlated with it no doubt were applied only to cases of things changing position relative to the surface of the earth. A caravan on land was said to move, a ship at sea was said to move, and in the sky the sun and stars were said to move. Looking at the actual talk of people before Copernicus, one might form the hypothesis (let us call this hypothesis A) that they were using the word "motion" to *mean* change of position relative to the surface of the earth. And perhaps if they had been asked they would have said that that was what they meant (though what a person says about how he uses a word is no more trustworthy than, for instance, what a tennis player says about how he moves while playing— it is possible to make mistakes in describing one's own activities). Then came Copernicus, who suggested that the earth itself is in motion around the sun, while the sun and stars are at rest. The opposition which this view provoked probably resulted partly from people's feeling that his suggestion was self-contradictory. If motion means change of position relative to the earth, then it is necessarily impossible for the earth itself to move.

Looking back on this dispute in the light of hypothesis A, someone might say (let us call this viewpoint A), "Well, it's just a matter of words. If by 'motion' you mean change of place relative to the surface of the earth, then the earth itself does not move. But if by 'motion' you mean change of place relative to the sun and stars, then the earth does move. It's a matter of arbitrary verbal convention: the word can be used either way, and neither way is more correct than the other." This view of the matter makes it sound as though the dispute between the Copernican and Ptolemaic doctrines were basically just a dispute about the choice of the word (granting, of course, that with the choice of a word there go emotional responses which may be helpful or harmful to organized religion, and also that the choice of a word may prove to be convenient or inconvenient for scientific thinking). This view of the matter makes it sound as though Copernicus would have been better advised just to coin a new word to express his findings; he could have said, for instance, that the earth *smoves* around the sun. This would have left the old word unchanged, and other people could have continued saying that the sun *moves* around the earth. Coining a new word, rather than arbitrarily altering the meaning of the old one, would have prevented ambiguity and misunderstanding (Galileo would then have had nothing to recant).

But this way of viewing the matter does not do justice to Copernicus's achievement. Copernicus would have made a less important contribution to thought than he did make if he had merely advanced the theory that the earth *smoves*; that would have been a valuable idea, but not a revolutionary intellectual advance, as was his idea that the earth moves. Let us consider another viewpoint (viewpoint B) from which the matter might be described. From this second viewpoint, it would be said that Copernicus did not arbitrarily change the meaning of the word "motion"; what he did, rather, was to draw upon a deeper latent tendency already present in the past usage. To be sure, people in the past tended to speak of something as moving if and only if it was changing position relative to the earth; but according to viewpoint B, a deeper tendency in their past usage was their tendency to speak of something as in motion when and only when it was changing position relative to the *average* position of *most* of the matter in its environment. Let us hypothesize (hypothesis B) that this latter is what was meant by the word "motion." According to viewpoint B, hypothesis B rather than hypothesis A gives the correct account of what the word "motion" meant. Why should it be said that hypothesis B describes a *deeper* tendency in past usage? Partly, at least, because on the basis of hypothesis B we can propose an explanation of why people should have tended to speak of something as in motion when and only when it was changing position relative to the earth: people spoke this way in earlier times because they supposed the earth to be very much larger and more massive than the heavenly bodies, so that only things moving relative to the earth seemed to them to be moving relative to the average position of most of the matter in the environment. By the sixteenth century, knowledge of how the sizes of the heavenly bodies compare with the size of the earth had improved, yet at first no one realized that this weakened the grounds for saying that the earth does not move. Copernicus then came along. Recognizing that the earth does change its position relative to the average position of most matter in its environment, he suggested his heliocentric theory; a theory which (according to viewpoint B) did not change the meaning of the word "motion" but instead showed people that they had mistaken opinions about what does in fact move.

Here we have considered viewpoint A, based on hypothesis A, which describes the geocentric-heliocentric controversy as essentially verbal and having to do with matters analytic and a priori, and we have considered viewpoint B, based on hypothesis B, which describes the controversy as one over a question of empirical, synthetic fact (viz., does or does not the earth change position relative to the average position of most of the matter in its environment?). What we need to realize is that neither of these two viewpoints is wholly right. The truth lies somewhere in between, though closer probably to B than A. Neither hypothesis A nor hypothesis B can be said to be definitely true: the use of the term "motion" prior to Copernicus was not so definitely governed by rules that we have any clear ground for decisively accepting one of these two hypotheses in preference to the other. What we can properly say, however, is that both these *tendencies* were latently present in the use of the word "motion" (the tendency to call a thing moving if and only if it changes position relative to the earth, and the tendency to call a thing moving if and only if it changes position relative to the average position of most of the matter in its environment), and we can say that the latter tendency is perhaps the deeper one. Presently we shall have occasion to consider cases in the philosophy of mathematics that are similar to this one.

EUCLIDEAN GEOMETRY

2

Egyptians
and Greeks The surveying of land in order to lay out the boundary lines of property was an important task in ancient civilizations, but especially so in Egypt. There the flooding waters of the Nile each year inundated the fertile areas, obliterating many of the previous year's boundary markers, so that each year the Egyptians had to outline the fields anew. Sometimes the problem was to reconstruct the boundaries of a field on the basis of partial information; for instance, if the shape of a field were known and if the markings along one side had remained intact while those along the other sides had been obliterated, then the problem would be to replace the markings along those other sides. Sometimes it must have been impossible to determine exactly where the last year's boundaries had been, and then the problem would be to lay out entirely new boundaries in a way that would create the desired number of fields having the proper relative areas. The Egyptians became skilled at their annual task of laying out these boundaries, and they must have discovered and employed many useful principles concerning lines, angles, and figures—such as the rule that the sum of the three angles of a triangle is equal to two right angles, and that the area of a parallelogram is equal to that of a rectangle having the same height and length.

The ancient Egyptians must have arrived at these principles through observation and experiment—that is, by inductive reasoning. Thus, they must have measured many triangles and many right angles and found almost always that the sum of the three angles of a triangle is very nearly equal to two right angles; moreover, whenever the sum of the angles of a triangle appeared to be appreciably different from two right angles there usually would have been some explanation of the discrepancy—the angles had not been carefully measured or the sides of the triangle were not good straight lines. Similarly, they must have measured the areas of many parallelograms and many rectangles (perhaps by seeing how many small squares would fit into each), and they must have found that almost always the area of a parallelogram came out to be just about equal to that of a rectangle having the same height and length; and that in those cases where there seemed to be some discrepancy, this could be explained away as due to faulty measurement or to faultily outlined figures. The Egyptians seem to have been satisfied with accumulating an empirical knowledge of points, lines, and figures which enabled them to solve problems about the location of boundary lines and the comparative sizes of fields, as well as problems of architectural design and constructional engineering.

The Greeks saw what the Egyptians could do, and became acquainted with their empirical principles. To this knowledge the Greeks gave the name of geometry—that is, earth measurement. But the Greeks, unlike the Egyptians, prized geometry not just for its practical utility but also for its theoretical interest; they wanted to understand geometry for its own sake. And they were not satisfied with the empirical approach; they wanted to find rigorous deductive proofs of the general laws about space that underlie all practical applications of geometry. For several centuries, Greek thinkers gave attention to geometry, discovering and proving more and more geometrical principles. Some Greek philosophers, especially Pythagoras and Plato, regarded geometry as having very great intellectual importance, for because of its purity and abstractness it seemed to them to have a kinship with metaphysics and religion. Then about 300 B.C. Euclid wrote his classic book, *The Elements,* in which he drew together and presented in systematic form all the main geometrical discoveries of his predecessors. This great book is one of the most influential classics in the literature of Western thought. Through ancient times, through the medieval era, and in the modern period right up into the nineteenth century, Euclid's *Elements* served not only as the textbook of geometry but also as a model of what scientific thinking should be.

Euclid's procedure   What are the distinctive features of Euclid's procedures? For one thing, he always formulates his geometrical laws in universal form.

He never discusses the properties of any particular and actually existing line or figure, but always is concerned only with the properties which *every* line or figure of such-and-such a kind will possess. Not only that, but his laws always are worded so as to be rigorous and absolute; they never are qualified as approximations. He says, for instance, that the sum of the angles of every triangle always is equal to two right angles; he does not qualify this by saying that it is approximately true or usually true—he presents it as something rigorously and absolutely true. More important still, Euclid is not content just to state a large number of these geometrical laws; he *proves* them. In fact, his whole book consists of proofs arranged in systematic order. Moreover, his proofs are not inductive; Euclid never asks us to measure the angles of actual triangles in order to see whether they add up to two right angles. He never concerns himself with actual experiments or observations like that. Instead, his proofs are deductive proofs by means of which he seeks to establish his conclusions with the rigor of absolute logical necessity.

But now, how much can be proved? At first blush, one might imagine that in an ideal treatise on geometry the author would prove every one of the geometrical laws that he formulates. A little reflection will show us that this may be too much to expect. A proof (at least in the ordinary sense of the word "proof") is a chain of reasoning that succeeds in establishing a conclusion by showing that it follows logically from premises that already are known to be true. We cannot have a proof unless we can start with one or more already known premises which serve as a basis upon which the proof is to rest. And it is difficult to see how any serious geometrical conclusions could ever be proved unless we could start from premises at least some of which are geometrical laws about points, lines, figures, and the like; Euclid certainly thought that geometrical premises are indispensable if geometrical conclusions are to be established. Suppose we grant that a geometrical conclusion can be proved only on the basis of premises at least some of which are geometrical; does this mean that we cannot expect to prove every geometrical law? What if we were to start with some geometrical laws, deduce others from them, then deduce still others from those; and finally deduce our original laws from those last ones? No doubt this could be done; no doubt each geometrical law can be deduced from other geometrical laws. So would not this amount to proving them all? Of course the answer is no, for such a supposed proof would commit the fallacy of reasoning in a circle (begging the question). Circular reasoning is not proof, for such reasoning does not succeed in establishing the truth of its conclusions.

We must remember that deduction is not the same as proof: to deduce a conclusion from premises amounts to giving a proof of the conclusion only if the premises are already known to be true (I can easily enough *deduce* the conclusion "All pigs fly" from the premise "All pigs are mammals and all mammals fly"; but this utterly fails to *prove* that all pigs fly). Thus it seems that some geometrical laws must remain unproved, if others are to be proved. That is, the laws of geometry will have to be divided into two groups: on the one hand, there will be a small group of laws which will not be proved, but which will be adopted as basic premises; on the other hand, there will be an indefinitely large group of other geometrical laws, each of which we hope will be rigorously provable by appeal to these basic premises. Euclid's *Elements* gives the name "postulates" to the first group of laws: these are laws about lines, angles, and figures, laws which Euclid regards as true, which he does not intend to prove, but which he will employ for the proof of other geometrical laws. The laws which are proved are called "theorems" (or in more old-fashioned terminology, simply "propositions").

Euclid's
postulates

Let us look at the five postulates that Euclid actually gives in his system. Let the following be postulated, he says:

1. A straight line can be drawn from any point to any other point.
2. Any finite straight line can be extended continuously in a straight line.
3. Given any point and any distance, a circle can be drawn with that point as its center and that distance as its radius.
4. All right angles are equal to one another.
5. If a straight line crosses two other straight lines so that the sum of the two interior angles on the one side is less than two right angles, then the two other straight lines, if extended far enough, cross on that same side of the first line where those angles are.

If we reflect upon the meaning of these postulates, we see at once how very different is Euclid's approach to geometry from the empirical, inductive approach which the Egyptians employed. Euclid's first three postulates make clear that he is not directly discussing any actual, concrete problems of earth measurement; for under actual surveying circumstances it is not true that a straight line can be drawn from every point to every other point. Obstacles (mountains, the sea, part of a foreign country) often intervene to prevent this. Nor is it true under actual surveying circumstances that a finite straight line always can be extended continuously in a straight line. Obviously in practice a vertical straight line can actually be extended only a short distance upwards and downwards, and even the drawing of horizontal lines must stop when impenetrable obstacles are encountered. Nor is it true that a circle always actually can be drawn with any given center and radius; obstacles are sure to prevent this if the radius is very large. But Euclid knew all that, of course; he simply was not interested in these practical limitations. His conception is that *in principle* a straight line can be drawn between any two points, whether we actually can do it or not; that in principle a straight line always can be extended in a straight line, whether we are actually able to do so or not; and that in principle a circle can be drawn with any given center and radius, whether we are able to do so or not. Thus, Euclid's conception is of a space within which there are no absolute obstacles and around which there are no absolute outer boundaries.

Euclid's fourth postulate may seem puzzling, because one may wonder whether it is not too trivial to be stated. If two angles are both right angles then of course they must be equal, it may seem; why does Euclid need to postulate this? If Euclid had said that all right angles are right angles, then he would indeed have said something too trivial to need to be stated as a postulate, for that remark is true merely by virtue of its logical form; it is a truth of logic, not a truth of geometry. However, Euclid's conception is that an angle is a right angle if it is an angle that can be obtained by setting up one straight line upon another in such a way as to make the adjacent angles equal. It does not follow from this definition, by mere logic alone, that you will always get angles of the same size when you do this. Hence, the fourth postulate as Euclid understands it is not true merely by virtue of its logical form, and since Euclid is going to make use of it later on in his proofs, it does need to be stated explicitly as a postulate.

The fifth postulate is a more complicated law than the earlier ones. Its meaning can be illustrated by means of a figure (see Figure 1).

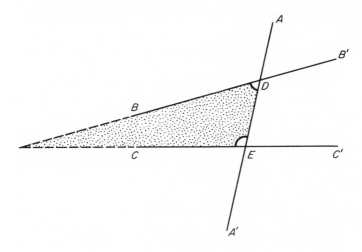

Fig. 1

Suppose we have three straight lines, AA', BB', and CC'. The postulate tells us that if AA' crosses both BB' and CC' and does so in such a way that the angles CEA and BDA' add up to less than two right angles, then *BB'* and *CC'* must sooner or later cross each other, if they are extended far enough.

**Euclid's
axioms and
definitions**   Besides the postulates, Euclid makes use also of five other initial principles which are called axioms (or "common notions"). The basic difference between the postulates and the axioms for Euclid seems to be that the postulates speak specifically about the subject matter of geometry (lines, angles, figures, and so on), whereas the axioms do not speak of anything specifically geometrical but are more general. The axioms have to do with equality of magnitude, a notion that can be used in discussing many subjects besides geometry. Euclid's axioms are these:

1. Things which are equal to the same thing are also equal to one another.
2. If equals be added to equals, the wholes are equal.
3. If equals be subtracted from equals, the remainders are equal.
4. Things which coincide with one another are equal to one another.
5. The whole is greater than the part.

Both the postulates and the axioms presumably are principles so clearly true that no sane person who understands them could doubt them for a moment. Such being the case, their lack of proof is nothing against them, and they can constitute the basis upon which the proofs of other far less obvious laws of geometry can rest. The Greeks probably would have thought that there was this difference between the axioms and the postulates as regards their believability: that if a person were to doubt or deny the postulates of geometry, he would of course be making a mistake and he would thereby disqualify himself for thinking about geometry; but he might nevertheless be able to think soundly about other subjects (such as arithmetic, biology, or music). Whereas, if a person were to doubt or deny the axioms about magnitude, he would thereby shows himself unfit for thinking about practically every serious intellectual subject; for all, or nearly all, subjects in one way or another employ the notion of magnitude.

Euclid wants to ensure that every one of his geometrical theorems is proved in a logically conclusive manner. But there is also another aspect to his search for rigor. Euclid is concerned, too, with systematizing the *terms* that occur in these geometrical laws, to make certain that the meaning of each of these terms is adequately fixed. It is a cardinal point of Euclid's method to try to see that each term is *defined* before being used, partly out of a pure desire for clarity and a wish to ensure that the meaning of each term is adequately fixed. But the purpose of this is also partly to aid in preventing logical fallacies in the proofs of theorems; for if we allow new, undefined terms to creep unnoticed into our theorems, this almost inevitably allows new and unstated premises containing those terms to creep unnoticed into our reasoning—with the result that we make the mistake of imagining that our conclusions follow logically from fewer premises than they do.

Here are some of the definitions which occur at the beginning of Book I of the *Elements*.

1. A *point* is that which has no part.
2. A *line* is breadthless length.
4. A *straight line* is a line which lies evenly with the points on itself.
5. A *surface* is that which has length and breadth only.
7. A *plane surface* is a surface which lies evenly with the straight lines on itself.
8. A *plane angle* is the inclination to one another of two lines in a plane that meet one another and do not lie in a straight line.
10. When a straight line set up on another straight line makes the adjacent angles equal to one another, each of the equal angles is called *right,* and the straight line standing on the other is called *perpendicular* to it.
14. A *figure* is that which is contained by any boundary or boundaries.
15. A *circle* is a plane figure contained by one line such that all the straight lines falling upon it from one point among those lying within the figure are equal to one another.
23. *Parallel* straight lines are straight lines which, being in the same plane and being produced indefinitely in both directions, do not meet one another in either direction.

Euclid's theorems The postulates, axioms, and definitions supply the starting point for Euclid's proofs. His aim is to prove all his other geometrical principles, first those of plane geometry and then later on those of solid geometry, by showing that they follow necessarily from the basic assumptions. In the *Elements* the things proved are of two kinds. Some are universal laws: for instance, Proposition 4 of Book I says, "If two triangles have the two sides equal to two sides respectively, and have the angles contained by the equal straight lines equal, they will also have the base equal to the base, the triangle will be equal to the triangle, and the remaining angles will be equal to the remaining angles respectively, namely, those which the equal sides subtend." Or Proposition 47 of Book I says, "In right-angled triangles the square on the side subtending the right angle is equal to the squares on the sides containing the right angle." However, there are other theorems that are not formulated as universal laws, but rather are expressed as tasks to be performed; a recipe for performing the task is worked out in such a way as to make it possible to prove that following the recipe will accomplish the task.

To get a glimpse of Euclid's method, let us look at his treatment of Proposition I, Book I.

On a given finite straight line to construct an equilateral triangle.

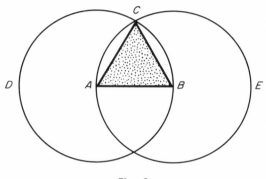

Fig. 2

Let *AB* be the finite straight line. Thus it is required to construct an equilateral triangle on the straight line *AB*. With center *A* and distance *AB* let the circle *BCD* be drawn (Postulate 3); again, with center *B* and distance *BA* let the circle *ACE* be drawn (Postulate 3); and from the point *C*, in which the circles cut one another, to the points *A*, *B* let the straight lines *CA*, *CB* be joined (Postulate 1). Now, since the point *A* is the center of the circle *CDB*, *AC* is equal to *AB* (by Definition 15). Again, since the point *B* is the center of the circle *CAE*, *BC* is equal to *BA* (by Definition 15). But *CA* was also proved equal to *AB*; therefore each of the straight lines *CA*, *CB* is equal to *AB*. And (by Axiom 1) *CA* is equal to *CB*. Therefore the straight lines *CA*, *AB*, *BC*, are equal to one another. Therefore the triangle *ABC* is equilateral; and it has been constructed on the given finite straight line *AB*.

We shall refer back to this proof presently; for the moment let us regard it merely as an illustration of Euclid's way of using postulates, axioms, and definitions to establish his theorems.

A modern view of deductive systems   Let us now think a little more about Euclid's basic way of organizing his system. Though Euclid clearly recognized the need for unproved postulates in his scheme, he seems not to have believed that there must also be undefined terms. The *Elements* contains no list of undefined terms, but, on the contrary, Euclid attempts to define all the terms he uses. And yet, once we reflect on it, we can see that the attempt to define within the system every geometrical term used within the system, like the attempt to prove every geometrical law within the system, is impossible. It must result either in a vicious circle or in an infinite regress. Thus, it would have been desirable if Euclid had been explicit about dividing his terms into two groups, those defined by means of other terms of the system and those not so defined (the latter nowadays are called *primitive* terms). Yet even though he was not explicit about this, if we examine his procedure we can see that his definitions are not all alike. Some of them (such as 1, 2, and 4) are vague elucidations in which terms that do occur in his postulates and theorems are partly explained by means of other terms that do not really belong to the system (that is, they never occur in postulates or theorems). These definitions are never made use of by Euclid in his proofs. Many other definitions (such as 10, 15, and 23) explicitly relate some terms of his system to others also occurring in the system; these definitions are used in Euclid's proofs. We may think of the terms introduced by the former sort of definitions as being Euclid's primitive terms and the terms introduced by the latter sort of definitions as being his defined terms. Unfortunately, however, in some cases it is hard to tell whether a term being defined should be regarded as primitive or not. Definition 8 is an example of this: should the term "inclination" be regarded as a primitive term of the system by means of which "plane angle" is explicitly defined; or should the term "plane angle" be regarded as a primitive term of the system with the term "inclination" serving as a term from outside the system used merely to elucidate it? Euclid does not make it easy for us to tell.

From a more modern point of view, we might say that in drawing up a system like this there are two basic decisions to be made, and made clear, at the start. The first decision has to do with terms. If the subject that we are systematizing is geometry, then looking over the whole array of terms (some writers prefer to speak of concepts) that occur in it, we must choose some list of them to serve as our primitive terms. In geometry there are scores of terms. We must decide just which of these terms are to count as primitive in the particular system being organized. Naturally we would hope that the list of primitive terms would be such as to permit us to define all or most of the other terms of the subject.

The second basic decision to be made has to do with the choice of axioms or postulates. Euclid's distinction between axioms and postulates is not retained by modern writers, who now mostly use the words "axiom" and "postulate" interchangeably. In making this second decision, we think of the totality of laws that can be expressed by using our primitive and defined terms, and we select a limited list of them to serve as our unproved assumptions, on the basis of which our theorems are to be proved. These unproved assumptions are all called axioms (or else are all called postulates).

How much leeway can legitimately be allowed in the choice of primitive terms, of definitions, and of axioms for a system? Some of the ancient Greeks seem to have thought that these choices were entirely determined by the nature of the subject matter. Aristotle, for example, speaks as though he felt that every science had its own definite first principles (which should function as the postulates), its own definite primitive terms, and even that for every defined term there was just one correct way of defining it. Euclid expresses no opinion on such questions. But from a modern point of view considerable leeway would be recognized here: there may well be alternative choices of primitive terms, of definitions, and of axioms that will lead to somewhat different yet equally legitimate formulations of the same subject matter. For example, in the modern axiomatic treatment of Euclidean geometry devised by the German mathematician Hilbert, the six primitive terms "point," "line," "plane," "incident," "between," and "congruent" appear. In a very different axiomatization worked out by Oswald Veblen a few years later only the terms "point," "between," and "congruent" are used, and his set of axioms is quite different from Hilbert's. Still different is the axiomatization due to E. V. Huntington, who used only the terms "sphere" and "includes" as his primitive terms; and whose set of postulates naturally had to be different again. Yet, different though these axiomatizations are, all of them are formulations of the same subject matter of Euclidean geometry, for in all of them the same Euclidean theorems can ultimately be proved. From a modern point of view these all are perfectly legitimate axiomatizations, though progressively more elegant as regards their basic choices of terms and axioms, since the later axiomatizations employ fewer primitive terms and axioms than did the earlier ones.

The motive for axiomatizing   In the *Elements*, Euclid aimed to strengthen our knowledge of points and lines and figures by increasing the rigor with which already known laws could be proved; he also aimed to extend this knowledge by proving new and hitherto unknown laws. Euclid sought to organize geometry in a systematic deductive form because by doing so he could increase the rigor of his proofs and also make it easier to prove new laws. But this could hardly have been the whole of his motivation, and certainly it is not the whole motivation of modern axiomatizers of geometry. For Euclid and they introduce refinements going beyond what would be called for, were the aim merely that of proving beyond all reasonable doubt that certain laws of geometry hold. The deductive organization of axioms and theorems also serves another purpose, that of displaying the laws of geometry in an elegant and perspicuous way, exhibiting interesting logical connections among them. This further purpose, so typical of mathematical thinking, is what makes Euclid sometimes take pains to prove things that his readers think obvious. This discovery of new logical connections is what impels modern axiomatizers to seek more elegantly economical axiomatizations of the subject matter.

Actually, there are opposite pressures at work, both with regard to choosing the set of primitive terms and choosing the set of axioms. On the one hand, it is desirable to make both these sets of choices in as economical a way as possible: a system is more elegant the simpler is its list of primitive terms and the simpler is its list of axioms. On the other hand, neither our list of primitive terms nor our list of axioms can just be cut arbitrarily short, for if the axioms selected are too few and too weak or contain too meager an array of primitive terms, then the theorems deducible will be insufficient to make the system interesting. A well-constructed system must strike an efficient compromise between these two opposite pressures; it should employ a comparatively economical set of primitive terms and axioms, and select these so that from them an appropriately rich array of theorems can be deduced. A system that lacks economy cannot give us much insight into the logical interconnections of its sentences, nor can a system do so if it lacks deductive power. But by combining a comparatively great economy with comparatively great deductive power, it maximizes the amount of insight which it can give us into the logical structure of its subject matter; thus it satisfies our intellectual drive to wring meaning out of multiplicity by reducing the latter to simplicity.

We use definitions to increase the deductive power of the system. By deploying a larger vocabulary we are able to prove theorems containing other terms besides the primitive ones, while yet keeping the list of primitive terms and axioms economical. What should be demanded of these definitions? When Euclid defines a right angle as he does, is he giving the correct definition? Wouldn't some people perhaps think that "equal to 90 degrees" is a better definition of a right angle? Here again the modern point of view is that there may well be many different and equally legitimate definitions of a term such as this. From the modern point of view, the one fairly firm requirement is that the definition of an established term like this should be such as to preserve the truth of all true geometrical sentences in which the term occurs, and to preserve the falsity of all false ones. So far as concerns the truth and falsity of assertions about right angles, it makes no difference whether the term "right angle" is defined as Euclid defined it or is defined as meaning an angle of 90 degrees. But of course Euclid's definition is more appropriate for his purposes, since the economy of his system would be diminished if he were to introduce primitive terms relating to the numerical measurement of angles.

Geometry
as a priori
knowledge

Euclid's system of geometry was an intellectual achievement of the highest importance, but it raised serious problems for philosophers. It would seem that Euclid's theorems about points, lines, and figures are to be regarded as purely logical consequences of his postulates. But what is the status of the postulates? Are they truths which we can know to be true? And if so, are they empirical truths or a priori truths? What kind of knowledge are they, and how do we know them to be true? Euclid himself simply did geometry, he did not write about such philosophical questions as these concerning the significance of geometry. But both ancient and modern philosophers have concerned themselves with these issues; and at least until the nineteenth century, there was an important measure of agreement among them about some basic points.

Up at least until the nineteenth century, thinkers who considered geometry took for granted that Euclid's postulates and theorems do have the kind of meaning that makes them capable of being significantly asserted or denied. In other words, they took for granted that one would be saying something true or false if one asserted or denied any one of these postulates or theorems. This point seemed so obvious to them that they hardly discussed it. They would have thought it absurd to suggest that Euclid's principles are empty formulas incapable of truth or falsity. They regarded geometry as a science, whose subject matter consists of points, lines, figures, and so on; and to say something about points, lines or figures is to speak either truly or falsely—there can be no third alternative here, they would have felt. Moreover, they felt no doubt but that in asserting Euclid's postulates and theorems one would be making true statements, while in denying them one would be making false statements. Euclid's postulates and theorems all are genuine principles of the science of geometry, principles which correctly describe points, lines, and figures, they thought. Euclid's geometry was accepted as a body of scientific knowledge about the nature of space, knowledge which is perfectly true and firm. Furthermore, the great majority of thinkers would have agreed that geometrical knowledge is a priori knowledge, not empirical knowledge. They would have held that to assert Euclid's postulates and theorems is to make statements that are necessarily true and that need no support from sense experience, while to deny them would be to make statements that are necessarily false and whose refutation need not come from sense experience.

Plato offered a striking argument bearing on this issue. He maintained that our knowledge of geometrical truths cannot rest upon evidence drawn from sense experience, for through the senses we never are acquainted with any genuine points, straight lines, or figures. We never see points; what we see are dots that do have parts. We never see straight lines; what we see are lines always with some breadth and always a bit crooked. We never see a genuine circle or a genuine equilateral triangle; for the figures we see never are made of perfectly breadthless lines nor are they ever perfectly proportioned. Therefore, geometrical knowledge cannot be knowledge that rests upon evidence drawn from sensory observations, since there is no such evidence. Geometrical knowledge must be a priori, not empirical, if this argument is correct.

Many later philosophers were deeply impressed by Plato's line of reasoning. His argument is not conclusive, however. For one thing, it is not clear that Plato is correct in claiming that we never observe genuine instances of points, lines, and figures. Suppose I am sitting in a large room whose walls are white and whose ceiling is blue; I look at the line where the surface of the wall meets the surface of the ceiling. So far as I can see, this is a perfectly straight line—it has no perceptible breadth and there is no perceptible crookedness. To be sure, if scientists came with their instruments and carefully measured the intersection of wall and ceiling, they probably would find that the transition from white to blue is not breadthless and that the line of intersection is not without crookedness. Probably they would find this, but is there any certainty that they must necessarily find this? Might it not be the case that however closely scientists examined the intersection, it still would look breadthless and without crookedness? There does not seem to be any convincing reason why we must believe that the lines we actually observe never are perfect straight lines. If we may say this of lines, then of course the same may be said of figures; and a point can simply be regarded as the intersection of two lines.

Moreover, even if we never did observe anything that actually was a perfect straight line, still that would not prove that our knowledge of points, lines, and figures could not be empirical knowledge. It is not an uncommon thing in science for empirical statements to be made concerning things of which no instances are observed. For example, a physicist can discuss how a pendulum would move that was swinging in a perfect vacuum with no friction at the pivot. There are no such pendulums: every actual pendulum encounters atmosphere and friction. Yet statements about how this ideal pendulum would move are empirical statements testable by experimentation upon actual pendulums. The notion of an ideal pendulum that encounters no atmosphere and no friction is a 'limiting concept' in this sense: to speak of how an ideal pendulum would move is to speak of the limit which the motion of actual pendulums approaches as their pivotal friction decreases and as the atmosphere in which they swing becomes more and more rarefied. Plato's line of reasoning neglects the possibility that statements about points, lines, and figures might be empirical statements in the indirect sort of way in which statements about ideal pendulums are empirical.

Thus, this particular argument of Plato's does not suffice to prove that geometrical knowledge is a priori. But there is another line of argument which is somewhat stronger, an argument whose most influential formulation comes from Kant. Kant argued that Euclid's postulates and theorems about points, lines, and figures cannot be empirical because they differ too much from empirical generalizations. According to Kant, Euclid's postulates and theorems possess a universality, and, closely connected with that, a necessity, which no empirical generalization can possess. Consider, for example, the principle that the sum of the angles of a triangle is equal to two right angles. If our knowledge of this principle were the result of empirical generalization, then the most that we could really know about it would be that *most* triangles (we have observed only some of them, and so could not claim any strong certainty with regard to *all*) have angle-sums that *differ little* from the sum of two right angles (our measurements always contain a margin of error, so we could not say with any certainty that these sums are *exactly equal*). Kant urges, however, that we really do know that the sum of the angles of every triangle is exactly equal to the sum of two right angles. Our knowledge of this principle possesses universality in the sense that we know there are no exceptions whatever, not even slight exceptions. Furthermore, if our knowledge were based on empirical generalization, then collecting additional observational evidence always would tend to increase the degree of certainty (or we may call it the degree of probability, if we prefer) which the generalization has for us. The more triangles we were to measure, the greater would become our right to feel assured that the law holds. Kant maintains that this does not happen. Our knowledge of this principle is not strengthened by the observing of further confirmatory instances, for we know ahead of time that the principle is necessary—that every triangle *must* have an angle-sum equal to two right angles. The certainty with which we know this excludes the possibility of our having reached it by empirical generalization. Kant's argument is a valuable one, but not absolutely decisive. We shall return later to this question of whether geometrical knowledge is a priori knowledge.

Geometry as synthetic knowledge There is one important further point regarding the status of Euclid's postulates and theorems that would have been accepted by most thinkers up until the nineteenth century, at least. Most of them would have felt that Euclid's postulates, as well as all the more important theorems that follow from them, are a priori truths having the kind of content which, in philosophers' language, makes them synthetic rather than analytic. If, like Kant, one regards logical truths as the basic examples of truths that are analytic rather than synthetic, then one can express this point about geometry by saying that there is an important difference between the non-trivial synthetic truths of geometry and the trivial analytic truths of logic.

What is the justification for holding that the laws of geometry are synthetic rather than analytic? How, if at all, could this be established? When there is a dispute over whether some kind of statement is analytic or synthetic, the person who maintains that it is analytic is in a somewhat better position to prove that he is right, for sometimes there can be a clear proof that a statement is analytic. As we saw in the first chapter, such a proof would consist in showing, by appeal to nothing but explicit definitions and principles of formal logic, that the given statement is equivalent to a logical truth. The existence of such a proof is sufficient (and many philosophers would think of it also as a necessary) condition of a statement being analytic. But now, to hold that a statement is synthetic is to hold (at least) that no such proof can be constructed. How could one ever prove that no such proof can be constructed? This kind of negative thesis looks very hard to establish; it scarcely seems as though there could be any formal proof that a statement is synthetic.

At any rate, Kant, the philosopher who is the most explicit advocate of the doctrine that geometry is synthetic, does not even attempt to prove this thesis in any formal sort of way. He simply asks us to reflect upon the meaning of our basic geometrical laws; he thinks it is self-evident that they are not merely verbal truths and that they cannot be shown to be equivalent to empty logical truths. His view would be that there do not exist definitions of the primitive terms of geometry that could enable us to transform the postulates into statements true merely by virtue of their logical form.

Of course some true statements about points, lines, and figures are analytic; even Kant would have had to admit that. For example, it is analytic in Euclid's system of geometry that all circles are figures, for this is a consequence of Euclid's definition of the term "circle." But

Kant would have maintained that the more basic laws of geometry are synthetic. Presumably he would have wanted to regard as synthetic all postulates and theorems that are couched solely in the primitive terminology of Euclid's system, and also all other theorems whose proofs essentially depend upon appeal to postulates or earlier theorems that are couched solely in the primitive terminology of the system. This presumably would include the great majority of Euclid's geometrical laws.

If the postulates of geometry and the more basic theorems all are synthetic in nature, this leads on to the question, how are our minds capable of possessing this sort of geometrical knowledge? Synthetic knowledge depends on something over and above mere understanding of the meanings of terms; and philosophers (before the nineteenth century) generally agreed in rejecting sense experience as a possible basis for this knowledge. It seemed, then, that something stranger, some odder kind of mental insight, must be at the root of our knowledge of geometry if our knowledge is synthetic and a priori.

In discussing geometrical knowledge some philosophers, such as Descartes, were content simply to speak of the mind's wonderful power of rational insight into the nature of geometrical matters, a power which is often compared to vision. It is a kind of 'seeing' with the 'eye of Reason.' Descartes speaks of rational insight, but offers little or no account of why the mind has this power or of the status of the things the mind has insight into.

Plato was less reticent. He, too, felt that in its knowledge of geometry the mind is exercising a very important kind of rational insight. But he proposed a theory about this insight. In one of his dialogues, the *Meno*, Plato represents Socrates as calling in an uneducated slave boy and asking him questions about a geometrical problem. Simply by asking the boy questions, rather than telling him anything (at least, not outright), Socrates brings the boy to give the correct answer to the geometrical problem. Socrates then gives his interpretation of what has happened. Since the boy was told nothing by Socrates, and since he never had been taught geometry, it must have been Socrates' questions that led the boy to *remember* geometrical knowledge which he possessed all along, but had forgotten. Socrates offers this as confirmation of his belief in the pre-existence of souls. The boy is remembering geometrical principles that he knew before birth. Before birth his soul was not yet imprisoned in its tenement of clay and was not befuddled by the confusing and misleading action of the senses; then his soul dwelt in a pure, immaterial, and unchanging realm, where eternal geometrical reality could be contemplated directly. Thus, the theory that Plato puts in Socrates' mouth is the theory that our present capacity to know the laws of geometry results from our having existed earlier in a different metaphysical state, where we had opportunity to contemplate perfect points, lines, and figures; now, if we make enough of an intellectual effort, we can succeed in remembering what we then saw face-to-face.

Kant offers a different theory about why the human mind can have insight into the laws of geometry. This insight, according to him, is not at all a matter of the mind's knowing about anything external to itself; it is entirely an internal insight by the mind into its own 'form of sensibility.' All sensations excited in the mind by external influences are endowed by the mind with Euclidean spatial form; this is simply the way the mind's faculty of sensation happens to work, Kant maintains. The mind is capable of gaining insight into its own mode of functioning and thus can grasp that everything which it could possibly sense must be spatial and must conform to Euclidean laws. Thus is attained the knowledge that Euclidean laws of space hold universally and necessarily of everything—of everything, that is, as the human mind senses it. However, external things as they are in themselves are not really spatial, Kant holds; certain contradictions which he calls *antinomies* force him to the conclusion that nothing could really be spatial, and that the spatial appearance of things is merely appearance introduced by the mind. But it is the task of science to study the world as it appears to us, not the world as it is in itself (the latter is in fact unknowable by us, according to Kant). Kant feels that his theory explains how geometry can be a science; that is, it explains how we are capable of possessing synthetic a priori knowledge of the spatial form of the world as it appears to us.

Using some traditional philosophical terminology, we might describe Plato's theory as a *realistic* theory about the objects of geometrical knowledge; for Plato holds that these objects have real being outside our minds, although they are inaccessible to sense experience. We might describe Kant's theory as a *conceptualistic* theory, since he holds that the objects of geometrical knowledge are real but have their reality only within the mind. Later in the next chapter we shall return to this problem.

NON-EUCLIDEAN GEOMETRY

3

Euclid's   Since Euclid's time, many people who have studied the *Elements*
fifth   have been troubled by Euclid's fifth postulate. The fifth postulate
postulate   seems anomalous. Even if our view is that the primary purpose of
organizing geometry into a rigorous deductive system is just to
exhibit in a perspicuous and elegant way the logical interrelations of the
principles of the subject, still the fifth postulate looks out of place on
account of its intricacy. It requires a much more complex sentence for
its formulation than does any of the other postulates, and in its intricacy it closely resembles some of the theorems that Euclid proves
(one of Euclid's theorems is the logical converse of the fifth postulate).
We would have a more attractive system if we could eliminate the
fifth postulate. Moreover, if we think as the Greeks did that the purpose
of organizing geometry in rigorous deductive form is also that of
establishing the truth of the theorems, then we shall especially want
to have postulates that are as obviously and surely true as possible—for
the degree of credibility which the theorems attain through being
deduced from the postulates cannot be greater than the degree of
credibility that the least credible postulate has in its own right. From
this point of view, the fifth postulate seems anomalous because it does
not have nearly as strong an air of obvious self-evidence as have the
other four postulates. Being far more intricate than the others, it is
less clearly true.

Down through the centuries, many different thinkers who were
dissatisfied with the fifth postulate tried to find ways of eliminating it:
ways of showing that it does not need to be regarded as a postulate.
Ideally, they would have liked to show that the fifth postulate is not

independent of the others; that is, that it can be proved as a theorem by reasoning which assumes the first four postulates alone (together with the axioms and definitions, of course). Or, failing this, they would have liked to show that at any rate Euclid's fifth postulate can be replaced by some other simpler and more self-evident principle which could serve as a new fifth postulate, so that Euclid's old fifth postulate could be deduced as a theorem and would no longer be needed as a postulate. Greek and Arabic commentators on Euclid made a number of attempts to eliminate Euclid's fifth postulate by proving it as a theorem, but always their work failed to be satisfactory. In each case either the supposed proof contained some outright logical mistake, or else it covertly assumed some geometrical principle just as intricate as Euclid's fifth postulate itself.

Attempted proofs like these did succeed in bringing to light that there are various other geometrical principles any one of which could do the logical job that Euclid's fifth postulate does (the job, that is, of combining with the other four postulates to permit the deduction of theorems). For example, the principle that from a point not on a given line one and only one line can be drawn parallel to the given line is a principle which could do the job that Euclid's fifth postulate does (this principle, called Playfair's axiom, was substituted for Euclid's fifth postulate in a widely used eighteenth century version of Euclidean geometry; for this reason Euclid's fifth postulate itself sometimes is a bit misleadingly referred to as 'the parallel postulate'). Also the principle that the sum of the angles of a triangle equals two right angles is another principle capable of doing the job that Euclid's fifth postulate does; and still another is the principle that given any three points not on a straight line there is just one circle that passes through them. These are three among the various principles, any one of which could be substituted for Euclid's fifth postulate without weakening the array of theorems that would be deducible. But there is no reason to hold that any of these alternative principles is significantly simpler than is Euclid's fifth postulate itself.

Sacchieri   The direct way of showing the fifth postulate to be not independent of the other postulates would be to construct a proof of the fifth postulate, using no premises except the other postulates (and the axioms and definitions). This was the approach tried without success by several Greek and Arabic commentators on Euclid. Another way of demonstrating the fifth postulate to be not independent of the others would be to employ the indirect method of reasoning called *reductio ad absurdum*: assume for the sake of argument that the fifth postulate is independent of the others and then show that this assumption leads to a contradiction and therefore must be false.[1] This was the method which the Italian Sacchieri tried in the eighteenth century. To suppose that Euclid's fifth postulate is independent of the others is to suppose that it would be logically possible for all the others to be true but the fifth postulate false. This was Sacchieri's approach: to start with, he assumed that Euclid's first four postulates were true (he added to them the assumption that any straight line can be extended so as to be as long as you please—this assumption is suggested by Euclid's second postulate, but is not explicitly contained in it); and he assumed for the sake of argument that the fifth postulate was false. He then considered a line *AB* at whose endpoints perpendiculars of equal lengths, *AC* and *BD*, are erected.

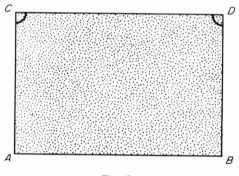

Fig. 3

On the basis of his assumptions, he was able to prove that in every such quadrilateral, angle *ACD* must equal angle *BDC*. With regard to these angles, which he called 'summit' angles, there arise three hypotheses: either (i) in all such quadrilaterals the summit angles are right angles; or (ii) in all such quadrilaterals the summit angles are obtuse angles; or (iii) in all such quadrilaterals the summit angles are acute angles. One and only one of these hypotheses must be correct, assuming that space is always the same, so that whatever is geometrically true of figures at one time and place is always true of figures everywhere. On the basis of his assumptions, Sacchieri was able to show that Euclid's fifth postulate must be true if hypothesis (i) is; and since he was assuming the falsity of the fifth postulate, he set aside hypothesis (i). On the basis of his assumptions, he showed that hypothesis (ii) can be set aside also, for it is inconsistent with the assumption that a straight line can be extended to any desired length. This left only the third hypothesis. Sacchieri did his best to show that hypothesis (iii) was in-

---

[1] For an account of *reductio ad absurdum* reasoning, see Wesley C. Salmon, *Logic*, pp. 30-32, Prentice-Hall Foundations of Philosophy Series.

compatible with his assumptions, and he believed that he was justified in setting it aside after finding that it led to some strange consequences. But he was unsuccessful in finding any strict logical impossibility that it led to. If he had succeeded in showing that (iii) was logically incompatible with his assumptions, that would have completed his proof: for then he would have obtained the contradiction which the *reductio ad absurdum* method seeks. The contradiction would have been that at least one of his three hypotheses must be true, yet that none of them would be true on his assumptions. This would have meant that his assumptions could not all be true together, and that in turn would have proved that the fifth postulate cannot be independent of the others. Sacchieri failed to achieve his purpose, but actually, without realizing it, he did succeed in doing something very different and highly important. For in trying to demonstrate the absurdity of hypothesis (iii), he deduced a variety of consequences from it, consequences which were parallel to, yet strangely unlike, the theorems of Euclidean geometry. Without understanding the significance of what he had done, Sacchieri had actually proved a number of the fundamental theorems of an entirely new type of geometry.

Lobachevskian geometry   It was not until the nineteenth century that mathematicians came to understand the logical situation, and came to realize that Euclid's fifth postulate really is independent of his others, which means that there can be logically consistent systems of geometry that in place of Euclid's fifth postulate contain some contrary postulate instead. During the earlier part of the nineteenth century three different mathematicians, without being in touch with one another, and all of them unaware of Sacchieri's work, independently developed a new type of geometry. The German mathematician Gauss, although he did not publish his thoughts on this matter, was probably the first to grasp the logical possibility of a geometry different from Euclid's; Gauss introduced the term "non-Euclidean geometry" to describe a type of geometry which is in effect that of Sacchieri's acute-angle hypothesis. The Russian mathematician Lobachevsky and the Hungarian Bolyai independently published accounts of this same type of geometry. Unlike Sacchieri, who had regarded his acute-angle hypothesis as absurd, these mathematicians were consciously developing what they regarded as a new type of logically consistent geometry.

The principles of this new geometry were strange and different from those of Euclidean geometry. In this new geometry, through a point not on a given line always more than one line can be drawn parallel to the given line. Also, the sum of the angles of a triangle is always less than two right angles, and the amount by which it is less is proportional to the area of the triangle; triangles having unequal areas can therefore never be similar. Moreover, the ratio of the circumference of a circle to its diameter is always greater than π, and the ratio is larger the larger is the area of the circle. But, strange as these principles were, they were not found to contradict one another.

Riemannian geometry   Later in the nineteenth century the German mathematician Riemann, and independently Helmholtz, developed another type of geometry which in effect corresponded to Sacchieri's obtuse-angle hypothesis. In it both Euclid's fifth postulate and also the assumption that a straight line can be extended to any desired length are denied. In it, for each straight line there is a maximum length to which the line can be extended. Through two given points always more than one straight line can be drawn. The sum of the angles of a triangle always is greater than two right angles, the excess being proportional to the area of the triangle. The ratio of the circumference of a circle to its diameter always is less than π and decreases as the area of the circle increases. Gauss's term "non-Euclidean geometry" came to be applied to the Riemannian as well as to the Lobachevskian type of geometry.

Actually, Riemann developed his conception not by means of the postulational approach, but by generalizing and extending a notion of 'curvature' that Gauss had developed. Gauss, in studying surfaces and the equations describing them, had made use of the notion of a *geodesic*—the line lying within a surface that is the shortest distance between two points on the surface. He showed that the nature of the geodesics for a surface depends upon a property of the surface which he defined and called 'curvature.' In a plane surface of course all geodesics are straight lines, and the surface is said to have zero curvature. On a spherical surface, too, all geodesics are alike—they are all arcs of great circles; the spherical surface is said to have uniform positive curvature, the amount of curvature being inversely proportional to the size of the sphere. On the surface of an egg, however, the geodesics would not all be alike but would differ for pairs of points lying in different regions of the surface and also would differ, depending on the orientation of the points, even within the same region; an egg-shaped surface is said to have positive curvature varying from place to place on it. A saddle-backed surface is said to have negative curvature.

Now consider a blind map-maker who is imprisoned on a surface so that he can move only within this surface, never above or below it. From his point of view, a 'straight line' could for practical purposes be identified with the shortest distance between two points. Then the 'geometry' of the surface (what the sum of the angles of a 'triangle' composed of three geodesics will be, and so forth) will depend on the curvature of the surface; any two regions of surface that are alike as regards the curvature there will be alike as regards their 'geometry.' Although the mathematical definition of curvature is not simple, curvature is something that can readily be visualized in connection with ordinary surfaces, and there is nothing paradoxical about it.

What Riemann did was to generalize Gauss's notion of curvature so that it could be applied also to three-dimensional space, enabling us to speak of the curvature of three-dimensional regions of space; meaning thereby the extent to which the 'geometry' of a volume of space differs from Euclidean geometry. We can describe Euclidean geometry as envisaging a space all regions of which are of zero curvature. Lobachevskian geometry envisages a space all regions of which are alike in having some constant negative curvature. And Riemannian geometry envisages a space all regions of which are alike in having some constant positive curvature. Of course this opens up the possibility of envisaging any number of other kinds of space in which the curvature is not constant everywhere.

This way of speaking does sound paradoxical, however. When the layman hears talk of the 'curvature' of space, he may imagine that he is supposed to visualize the curvature of three-dimensional space in just the same sort of way in which he can successfully visualize the curvature of surfaces within three-dimensional space. Perhaps the layman tries to imagine three-dimensional space somehow bent and twisted, perhaps in a fourth dimension. This sort of feat of imagination is as unnecessary as it is impossible. We must not suppose that mathematicians perform, or that they expect others to perform, any impossible feats of imagination. Both for two-dimensional surfaces and for three-dimensional volumes of space, the term 'curvature' is basically defined by reference to mathematical properties of the equations describing the behavior of geodesics. The notion makes perfectly good sense both in the less abstract case of surfaces, where we can readily visualize its significance, and in the more abstract case of volumes of space, where we cannot visualize it as meaning any literal sort of bending or twisting of all three dimensions.

The problem
of consistency

The development of Lobachevskian and of Riemannian geometries came as something of revolutionary intellectual significance. Earlier thinkers, and especially the philosopher Kant, had held that there was only one true geometry, whose laws were necessarily and immutably Euclidean. Was not that view clearly refuted by the appearance of these new types of geometry? But if mathematicians permit the development of alternative geometries whose laws contradict those of Euclidean geometry, what has become of the notion of truth in mathematics? Can it be that these conflicting geometries are equally true? Or is it that mathematicians no longer even seek the truth about space?

Many conservative-minded people were deeply puzzled by these questions and were deeply shocked by the working out of non-Euclidean geometries. They felt that Euclid's postulates and theorems were all true, and necessarily so; they felt that any non-Euclidean geometry must therefore contain what is necessarily false. And it seemed to them that a system of geometry must be logically inconsistent if it contains necessarily false postulates and theorems about space, such as that the sum of the angles of a triangle is less than, or greater than, two right angles. Yet no one ever succeeded in discovering either in Lobachevskian or in Riemannian geometry any pair of theorems that were strict logical contradictories of each other (that is, that contradicted each other by virtue of their logical form). Opponents of non-Euclidean geometry, although they tried hard, never were able to show that it violated the requirements of formal logical consistency. Yet these non-Euclidean systems had not positively been proved to be consistent either. The very important question whether they were consistent hung in the air for a time. The seriousness of this question was a powerful factor that forced mathematicians to seek still more rigorous logical procedures than those observed by Euclid. Another factor was their increasing awareness of logical weaknesses within Euclid's *Elements* itself.

Logical gaps in Euclid's "Elements"   For more than two thousand years Euclid's *Elements* survived all challenges and stood as a supreme mathematical achievement. Euclid's standards of rigor were admired as the highest possible and the cogency of his proofs was thought unsurpassable. But gradually more and more small criticisms began to accumulate. During the nineteenth century mathematicians' standards of rigor grew sharply higher, and it came to be realized that Euclid's work, admirable as it is, does contain many logical gaps. There are many places in Euclid's proofs where his stated assumptions are not sufficient to make his conclusions follow merely by formal logic alone. An example of one such logical gap is found in Euclid's proof of his Proposition I, which we considered in the preceding chapter. In that proof Euclid prescribes that two circles are to be drawn, one with center at point A and the other with center at point B, the distance between A and B to serve as the radius of each. He then immediately goes on to speak of the point C at which these circles intersect one another. But what logical reason does Euclid have for saying that there must be one and only one such point C? What right has he to suppose that the circles must intersect one another at all; or that if they do, they do so only once? Euclid uses no postulate from which this follows; he has no postulate that assures the *continuity* of lines and circles. Thus there is a logical gap in his reasoning; from the premises that he actually states, it does not follow by formal logic alone that there need be just one such point C. To supply what is needed, one might introduce an added postulate saying that if a line (such as *ACE*, the circumference) belongs entirely to a figure (here the plane) which is divided into two parts (outside and inside the circle) and if the line has at least one point in common with each part, then it must also meet the boundary between the parts. In order to fill the logical gap in Euclid's proof of his Proposition I some such additional postulate would have to be added to his system.

Why is it that Euclid himself and most of his readers down through the centuries did not notice this logical gap? The reason surely is that the figure which accompanies Euclid's Proposition I made it seem perfectly clear to them that there must be such a point C; it was so obvious that they never thought of asking for proof of it. The reader who looks at the figure finds Euclid's reasoning perfectly convincing, for it is impossible to visualize the two circles lying in the same plane without meeting in some one point C. This situation occurs often in Euclid's proofs: in many places his conclusions do not follow from his stated premises by formal logic alone, yet the reader finds the reasoning highly convincing because Euclid's book contains a diagram depicting the geometrical situation under discussion, a diagram which enables the reader to feel he sees that Euclid's conclusions must hold.

Is Euclid's reasoning *invalid* in cases where his conclusions fail to follow from the stated premises by pure logic alone? It would perhaps be overly severe to say that. Some philosophers and some logicians do occasionally speak as though they thought that no reasoning is really valid unless it is valid on account of its logical form alone; but that is an unduly extreme view. Many perfectly valid deductive arguments are not valid on account of their formal logical structure but rather on account of the particular meanings of nonlogical terms occurring in them; and it might be possible to regard Euclid's proofs in this light. However, these logical gaps nevertheless are very much to be deplored, even if they do not definitely mean that Euclid's reasoning is invalid. For these logical gaps are unintentional: it was simply because he was not aware of them that Euclid failed to close them— and the assumptions needed to close these gaps are not more trivial in content or in any way less worthy of being explicitly stated than are the postulates which Euclid explicitly sets forth. Euclid's goal when he set out to systematize geometry surely was to try to produce proofs that would be valid on account of their logical form alone (though he probably would not have described his goal in this way). Where his reasoning falls short of this, he is falling short of his intended goal, and his reasoning lacks the rigor which he and we would like it to have had.

The desire to correct these gaps in Euclid's proofs was one reason for the development of a stricter style of systematic presentation for geometry. Another even stronger reason was that in systematizing non-Euclidean geometry, it had become absolutely imperative to avoid gaps in reasoning, in order to assure the strict reliability of proofs. The consistency of non-Euclidean geometry was in doubt, so it was imperative to ensure that no non-Euclidean theorem should be deduced that did not strictly follow from the axioms. And of course with non-Euclidean geometries it is out of the question, anyway, to have diagrams to which we can reliably appeal in eking out gaps in the assumptions—since anyone using a diagram is likely to interpret it in a Euclidean rather than in a non-Euclidean fashion. Euclidean geometry had got along for two millennia without complete rigor in its proofs because no one challenged its consistency and because its diagrams comfortably filled gaps in the reasoning. Non-Euclidean geometry could be given the benefit of the doubt in neither of these ways.

For these reasons there gradually developed late in the nineteenth century a more rigorous conception of how a deductive system should be organized so as to avoid the sort of logical gaps that affect Euclid's presentation. The goal is to present proofs which are valid solely on account of their logical form. In order to attain this goal, the presentation has to be made in such a way that it can be regarded from a very cold and abstract viewpoint. It is not that in thinking about a system we need *always* adopt this abstract point of view; but the system is to be presented so that whenever we wish to examine the validity of proofs it will be readily *possible* for us to regard the system in a very abstract light. This point of view will be abstract in two ways.

First, when we are adopting it we shall pay no attention to whether the axioms and theorems are *true*, for that may distract our attention from the logical interrelations between them. The danger in Euclidean geometry is that we are inclined to feel very confident that certain theorems are true, and so we may on that account make the mistake of imagining that they follow from premises which do not rigorously entail them; and in non-Euclidean geometry there is the opposite danger, that when we are inclined to feel that a certain theorem is absurdly false this may blind us to the fact that it does rigorously follow from its premises. The remedy is to pay no attention to whether the axioms or theorems are true, but to focus attention solely upon their deductive interrelations.

Moreover, the approach is abstract in a second and more radical sense: when we adopt this viewpoint we are to pay no attention to the *meanings* of the primitive terms occurring in the axioms. The meanings of the geometrical terms have nothing to do with the formal logical validity of the proofs of theorems. Yet it is all too easy to allow oneself unconsciously to make use of assumptions that one does not realize that one is using, when one keeps the meanings of the terms clearly in mind. This is what happened to Euclid. (Some modern writers overstate this point, saying that for the sake of rigor one must regard the primitive terms of the system as *meaningless*. That is an overstatement, for rigor certainly cannot require us to imagine terms to be meaningless when we know quite well that meanings are attached to them. The point is rather that for the sake of rigor when considering proofs, we must pay no attention to whatever we know concerning the accustomed meanings of the primitive terms of the system).

Our goal is to construct the system so that every theorem will follow from the postulates by strict deductive logic—that is, on account of logical form alone. Our purpose in arranging the system so that it can be regarded from an abstract viewpoint is to ensure this goal. Thus, in principle, someone should be able to check the validity of each proof if he knows logic even if he does not understand the meanings of any of the terms of the system (and therefore, of course, has no basis for forming any opinion about the truth or falsity of any of the axioms or theorems). From this point of view, it is inappropriate to include in the system any definitions of the primitive terms; such definitions (such as Euclid's definition of a point as that which has no parts) have no influence whatever upon the validity of the proofs of the theorems and therefore are irrelevant to the system, when it is abstractly considered. Moreover, from this abstract viewpoint, the definitions of defined terms must be regarded merely as notational stipulations which allow us alternative ways of writing sentences. The definitions must be such as to show how any sentence of the system containing defined terms can be rewritten solely in the notation of the primitive terms of the system. Only when we are able to view the axioms, the primitive terms, and the definitions all in this abstract light can we be confident that our judgments about what logically follows from them are strict and rigorous.

It has become customary in recent decades to distinguish between what is called 'pure geometry' and what is called 'applied geometry.' Pure geometry would be geometry studied from the abstract point of view we have been discussing, whereas applied geometry would be geometry studied from a point of view that does attribute specific meanings to the terms. However, this way of speaking is slightly unfortunate, since according to it Euclid's work would presumably have to be classified as applied rather than as pure geometry, making it sound as though Euclid was not really doing mathematics, but was doing something perhaps more like engineering—a misleading suggestion. Let us speak instead about an *uninterpreted* system as contrasted with an *interpreted* system of geometry. We can then say that Euclid's *Elements* is put forward as an interpreted system (since Euclid surely had some fairly definite meanings in mind for his terms). But in light of what we have previously been saying, we should think of a geometrical system as uninterpreted when we are seeking to make a rigorous study of its logical structure. Especially with non-Euclidean geometries, it is important to think of them as uninterpreted systems when we are studying the proofs of their theorems. When we regard a system as uninterpreted, we take no notice of what meanings, if any, its primitive terms possess, and we take no notice of whether its axioms and theorems are true, whether they are false, or of whether they are neither true nor false (as will happen if the terms in them possess no specific meanings—for sentences are incapable of truth or falsity if the terms occurring in them lack meanings).

When we want to regard a geometrical system as uninterpreted, the safest and clearest procedure is to express the axioms and theorems in schematic form, replacing words like "point" and "line" by dummy letters, such as "*P*" and "*L*". Doing this helps us to avoid being influenced by the meanings that we normally associate with words like "point" and "line," and enables us to concentrate our attention upon the abstract logical structure of the system. To illustrate this approach, let us go back to Euclid's postulates as stated in Chapter 1, and let us consider the manner in which we might restate them if we wished to regard Euclid's system as uninterpreted (Euclid himself regarded it as an interpreted system, to be sure, but that need not prevent us from regarding it as an uninterpreted system).

Euclid's first postulate said that between any two points a straight line can be drawn. This amounts to saying that for any two distinct points there is a straight line to which each of them belongs. If we now restate this postulate in schematic form it can become:

1. For any two distinct *P*'s, there is an *S* to which each of them bears the relation *B*.

Here, instead of speaking of points we speak of *P*'s, instead of speaking of straight lines we speak of *S*'s, and instead of speaking of one thing belonging to another we speak of one thing bearing the relation *B* to another.

Euclid's second postulate said that any finite straight line can be extended in a straight line. This amounts to saying that for any straight line having two endpoints, there is another straight line to which both these points belong, but on which only one of them is an endpoint. If we now restate this postulate in schematic form it can become:

2. For any *S* such that there are two distinct *P*'s each bearing the relation *E* to it, there is another *S* to which each of those *P*'s bears the relation *B* but to which only one of them bears the relation *E*.

Here, instead of speaking of one thing being an endpoint of another we speak merely of one thing bearing the relation *E* to another.

Continuing in this way, we could restate all Euclid's postulates and definitions in this schematic manner; moreover, we could foresee how anything that can be said using Euclid's notions could be restated in our schematic manner. This puts us in an excellent position for studying the formal logic of Euclid's system. It is now easy to keep our viewpoint abstract as we investigate questions about the deducibility of conclusions from the postulates or about the correctness of proposed proofs. In investigating such questions we employ only the schematic versions of the sentences concerned, for we are interested solely in deductions that are valid purely by virtue of their logical forms. Consequently, we pay no attention to what "*P*," "*S*," and the other dummy letters mean—which is easy to do, since these letters have no particular meanings.

But now, suppose we have been regarding a system as uninterpreted, and have formulated its postulates, definitions, and theorems in this abstract schematic manner. Suppose we were now to decide that we wished to change our point of view, and turn the uninterpreted system into an interpreted one by assigning meanings to all of its dummy letters. Consider the schematic postulates (1) and (2) that were just used as illustrations. These contain the dummy letters "*P*" and "*S*," representing unspecified kinds of things, and the dummy letters "*B*" and "*E*," representing unspecified relations between things. One way of assigning meaning to these dummy letters is of course to let "*P*" mean point (in some specific sense), let "*S*" mean straight line (in some specific sense), let "*B*" stand for the relation between a point and a line when the point belongs to the line, and let "*E*" stand for the relation between a point and a line when the point is at the end of the line. When we interpret their dummy letters in this way, (1) and (2) can turn into Euclid's first and second postulates. But what we now must notice is that there are also innumerable *other* ways in which these dummy letters could be given meanings so that (1) and (2) would turn into meaningful statements and thereby become true or false.

For example, we might interpret "*P*" to mean straight line, "*S*" to mean point, "*B*" to mean the relation between a line and a point when the line ends at the point, and "*E*" to mean the relation between a line and a point when the line includes the point. Under this scheme of interpretation, (1) and (2) become the statements:

> For any two distinct straight lines, there is a point at which both of them end.

> For any point such that there are two distinct straight lines each including it, there is another point where both these straight lines end, but which only one of them includes.

These are meaningful geometrical statements, but, as it happens, they are both false, if the terms "point" and "straight line" are used in a normal sense.

It is also possible for us to interpret (1) and (2) in ways that do not even pertain to space. For example, we could let "*S*" stand for intervals of time (such as the twentieth century, the year 1492, or Plato's lifetime). We could let "*P*" stand for instants of time (such as the vernal equinox of 1888, or the beginning of the twentieth century). We could let "*B*" mean the relation between an instant and an interval when the instant belongs to that interval. And we could let "*E*" stand for the relation between an instant and an interval when the instant is the earliest or latest instant of the interval. Under this scheme of interpretation, (1) and (2) become the statements:

> For any two distinct instants, there is an interval to which each of them belongs.

> For any interval such that there are two distinct instants each either the earliest or the latest instant of that interval, there is another interval to which each of these instants belongs, but of which only one of them is the earliest or latest.

Here again we obtain two meaningful statements, but this time they have nothing to do with space. And, as it happens, this scheme of interpretation gives us two statements both of which are true. Of course innumerable other still different ways of interpreting (1) and (2) could be found; some would give us true statements and some would give us false statements.

We say that we have given an interpretation of an entire uninterpreted system when we have selected a meaning for each of the dummy letters occurring in its schematic postulates and theorems. So long as they remain uninterpreted, the schematic sentences are neither true nor false; but when every dummy letter has been given a meaning then each postulate and theorem becomes a statement that is either true or false. Usually an uninterpreted system will turn out to be such that under many interpretations some or all of its postulates and theorems become false statements, while under some other interpretations its postulates and theorems all become true statements.

Inconsistency   The opponents of non-Euclidean geometries had hoped to be able to show them inconsistent. Let us consider what this means. Inconsistency, in the sense that concerns mathematicians, has nothing to do with the special meanings that the terms in the system may possess; inconsistency has to do only with the abstract logical structure of the system. To say that a system is inconsistent is to say that two theorems which logically contradict one another both are deducible from the axioms of the system (let us now call them axioms rather than postulates). For example, suppose there were a system from whose axioms we could deduce the theorem "For each S there is a P to which it bears the relation R," and from whose axioms we also could deduce the theorem "There is at least one S which bears the relation R to no P"; these two theorems contradict one another, and this means that the system to which they belong is inconsistent.

Why should we care whether a system is inconsistent? The traditional answer is that consistency is important because of its connection with truth. With an interpreted system, the discovery of inconsistency would show that not all the axioms of the system are true. With an uninterpreted system, the discovery of inconsistency would show that there could be no way of interpreting it so as to make all the axioms come out true—and a system which cannot come out true under any interpretation is comparatively uninteresting.

How may we discover whether a system is consistent? The direct way of demonstrating inconsistency is of course to find two theorems which contradict one another on account of their logical form and each of which follows rigorously from the axioms. Demonstrating consistency may be more complicated, however. At this stage we may distinguish two somewhat different ways (later we shall consider a third). The first way would be to find an interpretation under which all the axioms (and consequently all the theorems) of the system do definitely come out true. The limitation of this first method is that it requires us to possess perfectly definite knowledge of the truth of the interpreted statements; only if there is no doubt about their truth can the proof of consistency be called a success. The second method of establishing consistency is to give a *relative* proof of consistency: we show that a given system is consistent provided some other, less suspect system is. This is done by showing that if there is any interpretation under which the latter system comes out true, then there must also be an interpretation under which the former system comes out true.

Using this second approach, mathematicians of the later nineteenth century made important progress with the question of the consistency of Lobachevskian and Riemannian geometries. They were able to establish that these non-Euclidean geometries must be consistent if Euclidean geometry is. To illustrate the idea behind this method, let us consider a way of dealing with Lobachevskian geometry that was informally suggested by the French mathematician Poincaré. Consider a sphere within which there is the following peculiarity: things inside uniformly shrink in size as they move away from the center, their shrinkage becoming proportionately greater and greater without limit as they approach the surface of the sphere. The inhabitants inside this sphere, along with their yardsticks, get smaller and smaller as they move outwards towards its surface, their steps get shorter and shorter, and they never reach it. In this sense, the interior of the sphere forms an infinite universe, from their point of view. Suppose they use the term "straight line" to mean the shortest distance between two points as measured with their yardsticks; and they interpret the other terms of geometry in appropriate corresponding ways, for instance, letting a 'triangle' be a figure formed by three such 'straight lines.' The geometry of their universe is now Lobachevskian. The sum of the angles of a triangle will always be less than two right angles, the more so the larger the area of the triangle; through a point not on a given straight line more than one straight line can be drawn parallel to a given straight line; and so on.

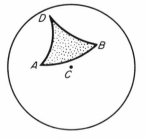

Fig. 4

For example, if C is the center of the sphere, then a 'triangle' drawn with vertices at points A, B, and D will have sides that curve because of the shrinkage of yardsticks (the sides of the 'triangle' are to be the shortest paths from vertex to vertex, as measured with yardsticks; and to lay down the yardstick the fewest times one must follow a curved path that tends to minimize the effect of the shrinkage of the yardstick). This is why the sum of the angles of the 'triangle' will be less than two right angles. Here we can discuss the matter only very informally, but the aim is to show that if Euclidean geometry is consistent then so must Lobachevskian geometry be. If Euclidean geometry is consistent, then this Euclidean 'model' of a universe that has been described must be logically consistent; and if so, then the principles of Lobachevskian geometry which we have interpreted so as to hold in our 'model,' must be consistent too.

What about the consistency of Euclidean geometry itself? In earlier centuries it had always been taken for granted that the postulates of Euclidean geometry, considered as an interpreted system, all are true; and therefore that the system is of course consistent (if the postulates all are true, then the theorems deduced from them must all be true too, so no theorem can contradict another). But the rise of non-Euclidean geometries made this seem more doubtful; perhaps we cannot be so sure that the postulates and theorems of Euclidean geometry are all true. What then can be done to establish the consistency of the Euclidean system itself? Even if we are not sure of the truth of Euclid's system, can we at least be confident of its consistency? To establish the consistency of Euclidean geometry relative to some other system of geometry would not be helpful, for any other system of geometry is at least as suspect as regards its consistency as is Euclidean geometry. What we can usefully do, however, is to establish the consistency of Euclidean geometry relative to our mathematical theory of real numbers. We take Euclidean geometry in its abstract, uninterpreted form and construct a numerical interpretation of it. Where Euclid spoke of points we now shall speak of triads of numbers (numbers of the kind called real numbers), where Euclid spoke of lines and figures we shall speak of certain sorts of sets of triads of numbers, and so on. Under our numerical interpretation the postulates and theorems of the system become statements about numbers, and these statements about numbers are true, if our accepted theory about numbers is correct. Thus we construct within number theory a 'model' of Euclidean geometry, and the fact that we can do this means that Euclidean geometry must be consistent if our mathematics of real numbers is consistent. Our problem about the consistency of geometry is thus transformed into a problem about the consistency of the mathematical theory of real numbers.

Non-Euclidean geometries have been developed and have been shown to be as logically consistent as Euclidean geometry. Does this decisively refute the traditional philosophical view which regarded geometrical knowledge as synthetic and a priori? The majority of writers of recent times who have dealt with the philosophy of geometry have held that it does. The existence of these non-Euclidean geometries as consistent mathematical disciplines has, it seems to them, decisively overthrown the traditional belief that the laws of Euclidean geometry are necessarily true and that in them we have synthetic a priori knowledge of our world. Among these recent writers, the most widespread view nowadays has come to be the view that geometry can be regarded in just two ways. Uninterpreted geometry (or 'pure' geometry), they hold, must be regarded as a study that involves purely analytic knowledge, for it considers only matters of pure logic—what follows from what. The knowledge deployed there is knowledge about logical deducibility, which rests on considerations of logical form. Interpreted geometry (or 'applied' geometry) must be regarded as considering hypotheses about nature which may or may not be true. According to this view, when we give specific meanings to the primitive terms, changing our viewpoint from that of uninterpreted to that of interpreted geometry, then inevitably the sentences of geometry become empirical hypotheses about the world. And the only way of deciding whether they are true or false is inductively, through observation and experiment. Is our actual world Euclidean, or is it Lobachevskian, like the sphere imagined by Poincaré? According to this view, we must experiment to see; that is the only way.

Now, to have an interpreted system of geometry we must choose specific meanings for the undefined primitive terms occurring in the system. For purposes of our discussion, it will suffice if we focus our attention on the term "straight line"—not that this is the only primitive term (indeed, as we saw, there even are axiomatizations in which it is not a primitive term at all). But it is a key term so far as interpretation goes, because once we have decided what it is to mean, it becomes comparatively easy to settle on allied senses for the other terms.

Let us now consider some of the ways in which the term "straight line" might plausibly be interpreted. There is no one absolute sense in which the term *must* be interpreted; but for our present purposes we are not interested in interpretations that are too far removed from normal usage. Let us consider a few plausible senses that the term could be given. Here the point is to describe ways in which empirical significance might plausibly be attached to this term, so that sentences containing it will now express true-or-false assertions. What might somebody be claiming about a line, when he claims that it is straight?

There are several different sorts of procedure in ordinary life that we use for determining whether a line is straight, and with them go several different notions of what it is for a line to be straight. In connection with Poincaré's example, we considered the notion that the shortest distance between two points is what is to be meant by a straight line. According to this notion, to see whether a line is straight we investigate whether it is the shortest path between its endpoints. This method requires that we possess means of measuring distance, such as the yardstick (the procedure being to pick up the yardstick and lay it down each time so that one endpoint will rest just where the other endpoint previously rested). The method is straightforwardly applicable only where we may assume that the yardstick does not expand or contract as it is moved about. If the yardstick is made of metal and the temperature varies greatly, then the thermal expansion will introduce errors—unless we make compensating corrections.

Another notion of what it is for a line to be straight comes from the practice of the carpenter, who sights along his plank to see whether it is straight or crooked. Here the underlying idea is that light travels in straight lines. The carpenter, of course, would not rely upon this method if the plank were lying half in and half out of water; the method can be used straightforwardly only where the medium through which one looks is uniform so that it does not refract the light. Here then is another basic notion of what a straight line is: the path of a ray of light through a medium of uniform refractive index.

Another, though less practical, conception would be that a straight line is the path along which a stretched cord tends to lie as the tension on the cord increases without limit. Still another conception would be that a straight line is the path along which a moving body subject to no external forces will travel.

Several fairly plausible ways of interpreting the term "straight line" have now been mentioned. Now, what kind of assertions do the sentences of an uninterpreted geometry become when we interpret them in one or another of these ways? It is clear that all these suggested interpretations will turn the sentences of geometry into empirical statements. Through a point not on a line, how many lines can be drawn parallel to the given line (that is, in the same plane as the given line but never intersecting it)? Whichever of the interpretations so far proposed be adopted, this question becomes an empirical question, to be settled by observation and experiment. Under all these interpretations, it is an empirical question whether the universe is Euclidean, Lobachevskian, Riemannian, or something else.

On the basis of the world-view of classical Newtonian physics, one would expect Euclidean geometry to come out true and the others to come out false when interpreted in any of these suggested ways. The Newtonian world-view leads us to expect, for example, that through a point not on the path of a given light ray, one and only one ray of light can travel parallel to the given ray (through a medium of uniform refractive index). It leads us to expect that when from three given points a triangle is laid out by finding the pathways along which a measuring rod must be laid down the fewest times, then no matter how big the triangle may be, the sum of its angles always will equal two right angles. Whichever of the suggested conceptions of a straight line we choose to employ, classical physics would lead us to expect the Euclidean system to become a set of true statements when interpreted that way.

Einstein's theory of relativity overturned that classical Newtonian world-view, however. Einstein's theory, now well supported by experimental evidence, leads to a very different set of predictions. According to Einstein's theory we must expect that every two rays of light within the same plane will meet sooner or later, if their paths extend far enough. Also, Einstein's theory predicts that if you were to lay out very large triangles letting their sides be paths along which measuring rods needed to be laid down the fewest times, then you would find that the sum of the angles of such triangles is greater than two right angles, and gets larger the larger the area of the triangle. Thus, when geometry is understood in this way, its statements are empirical, and the physical world proves to be Riemannian rather than Euclidean in its structure. (Strictly speaking, Riemannian geometry has space whose curvature is constant, whereas the space of the physical world proves to be always curved but not curved to the same extent everywhere.)

Interpreted geometry as a priori As we have seen, it certainly is possible to find ways of assigning meaning to the term "straight line" and to the other terms of geometry so that the axioms and theorems of geometry become empirical statements. Indeed, there are a variety of plausible ways in which this can be done (ways, that is, which are not sharply at odds with the normal usage of these terms). The ways we have so far considered turn many of the sentences of Euclidean geometry into untrue statements about the world, while making the sentences of Riemannian geometry come out true. To many philosophers this has seemed to settle the matter: space has been empirically proved to be Riemannian rather than Euclidean, they say; this is the ultimate, complete refutation of the outmoded Kantian philosophy of space. Such a view is hasty and unfair, however. Must an interpretation of a system of geometry turn its axioms into empirical statements? Is that the only possibility? Or is it also possible to interpret the axioms so that they become a priori statements?

Certainly there does remain a further style of interpretation of the term "straight line" and the other basic terms of geometry which needs to be considered—another way of understanding these terms which has deep roots in normal usage. This way of interpreting the term "straight line" does not tie its meaning strictly to any one type of experimental outcome, such as the path of a light ray or the path along which a yardstick is laid down the fewest times. According to this conception of a straight line, such observations do tend to indicate that a line is straight, but they are not conclusive on that score. According to this conception, it is an essential part of the meaning of "straight line" that a triangle whose sides are straight lines must have angles whose sum is equal to two right angles: if we find a triangle whose angles add up to more than this, that decisively shows that the sides of the figure are not really straight lines. According to this conception of geometrical terms, what we should say in describing the result of Einstein's theory of relativity is not that there are non-Euclidean triangles. Instead, we should say that, surprisingly enough, light rays do not travel in straight lines when passing through uneven gravitational fields; and that, surprisingly enough, yardsticks shrink in length and therefore have to be laid down oftener when used in strong gravitational fields. We already knew that light rays do not travel in straight lines through media of varying refractive index, and we knew that yardsticks expand and contract with varying temperature. What these findings of modern physics show, according to the conception we are discussing, is just that gravitational fields also can affect the paths of light rays and the lengths of yardsticks. New corrections must be introduced if we are to use light rays and yardsticks to determine straight lines through uneven gravitational fields. To be sure, these new corrections are of a special universal kind: different colors of light were differently refracted by the medium they pass through, and yardsticks of different materials are differently influenced by changes in temperature; whereas this new gravitational correction affects all light and yardsticks in just the same way. The universality of these corrections is not a decisive reason against our regarding them as corrections, however.

When we understand geometrical terms in this spirit, the sentences of geometry turn into a priori statements rather than empirical ones. The postulates and theorems of Euclidean geometry become necessarily true statements, while those of non-Euclidean geometry become

necessarily false statements. It must have been this way of regarding
geometrical terms that the German logician Frege had in mind when
(following Kant's line of thought) he wrote:

> . . . The truths of geometry govern all that is spatially intuitable,
> whether actual or product of our fancy. The wildest visions of
> delirium, the boldest inventions of legend and poetry, where animals
> speak and stars stand still, where men are turned to stone and trees
> turn into men, where the drowning haul themselves up out of swamps
> by their own topknots—all these remain, so long as they remain in-
> tuitable, still subject to the axioms of geometry.[2]

There is nothing absurd or definitely improper about this way of understanding geometry; it is a perfectly possible attitude to take. And this
is enough to show that the view discussed in the previous section is too
crude: the axioms and theorems of an interpreted geometry do not
have to be empirical statements; they may be a priori ones.

Confusion about this matter often arises because people get the
idea that if the postulates of some non-Euclidean geometry are true
then the postulates of Euclidean geometry cannot all be true. They
get the idea that Euclidean and non-Euclidean geometries are incompatible with one another and so cannot both be correct. This is a
mistake. People who have this idea do not fully realize that the postulates of a geometry are capable of truth or falsity only when they are
interpreted in some specific way; they do not fully realize that a pure,
uninterpreted set of postulates is neither true nor false. It is misleading
and confused to say, for instance, that the postulates of Riemannian
geometry are true—for actually the Riemannian postulates are true
under some interpretations and false under others. What we should say
is that Riemannian geometry is true when, for instance, the term
"straight line" is interpreted as meaning the path of a ray of light
through a medium of uniform refractive index (and the other terms
are interpreted in associated ways); or that Riemannian geometry is
true when "straight line" is interpreted as meaning the path along which
a measuring rod would have to be laid down the fewest times, assuming
the temperature of the rod to be kept constant (and the other terms
are interpreted in associated ways); or the like. It is equally misleading
and confused to say simply that the postulates of Euclidean geometry
are false—for the postulates of Euclidean geometry are true under some
interpretations and false under others. What we should say is that the
postulates of Euclidean geometry are false if we interpret "straight line"
to mean the path of a ray of light through a medium of uniform refractive index, or to mean the path along which a measuring rod kept

[2] Gottlob Frege, *The Foundations of Arithmetic,* trans. J. L. Austin (Oxford:
Basil Blackwell & Mott, 1953), p. 20e.

at constant temperature would have to be laid down the fewest times (and the other terms are interpreted in associated ways); but that the postulates of Euclidean geometry are true if we interpret "straight line" and the other terms in the fashion suggested in the preceding paragraphs, not tying their meaning strictly to any one physical phenomenon or procedure and treating it as an essential aspect of their meaning that the Euclidean principles must be satisfied.

Significance of the a priori interpretation   If it be granted that an a priori interpretation of geometry is possible that will make Euclidean axioms into necessary, a priori truths, two philosophical questions then arise. First, does this a priori interpretation constitute synthetic a priori knowledge in the traditional sense? And second, is this a priori interpretation preferable to empirical interpretations such as those mentioned earlier?

In dealing with the first question, let us consider the statement that the sum of the angles of a triangle equals two right angles. Let us construe this as an a priori truth—that is, a statement which we can know to be true without consulting experience, and which no new sensory observations could refute. Viewed in this spirit, is the statement synthetic or analytic? In dealing with this question it becomes of decisive importance to distinguish between the two different accounts given by Kant of the distinction between the analytic and the synthetic. Kant felt that his two accounts amounted to essentially the same thing; but they do not. Our example is synthetic, according to the second account of the distinction, for the statement is not true merely by virtue of its logical form, nor do we possess any definitions by appeal to which we can translate it into a statement true merely by virtue of its logical form. (Or, if you think that definitions are in our possession by means of which this patricular law could be translated into a statement true merely by virtue of its logical form, then we may retreat to a more basic thesis: under this a priori interpretation of geometry, *not all* the laws of Euclidean geometry can be translated into statements true merely by virtue of their logical form, for sufficient definitions for that purpose are not available). Yet, according to the first account of the distinction, our example would qualify as an analytic statement: for nothing other than understanding of it is required in order to enable us to know that it is true. To see that this is so, consider the imaginary case of someone who contemplated this statement yet was doubtful of its truth. How should we describe his intellectual condition? Should we describe his condition by saying that perhaps he does understand the statement perfectly well, but his faculty of Rational Insight is beclouded? That really would be an unsatisfactory description of the case. If he doubts the statement, his doubt is by itself sufficient to show that

he does not understand the statement (either he does not understand
it at all, or he understands it in some manner other than the manner
in which it is intended to be understood). If we meet someone who
has such a doubt, our proper procedure in removing the doubt is not
to urge him to blink the eye of his Reason and to focus it more in-
tently; it is unlikely that such advice would be of any use. What would
be of use is to offer hints about how we intend the sentence to be
understood.

When geometrical terms are understood in the spirit suggested
in the preceding section, it becomes a necessary a priori truth that the
sum of the angles of a triangle must equal two right angles. But knowledge of this does not constitute an insight gained by Reason through
some remarkable clairvoyant power—insight either into the ultimate
nature of reality or into the ultimate structure of the human mind. On
the contrary, this piece of knowledge reflects our determination to use
geometrical terms in a certain manner. It reflects our determination not
to *call* anything a triangle unless it has this character. Here the knowledge is based upon understanding of language, not upon insight into
nature or into the mind. Hence, the knowledge is analytic here in the
first of the two senses discussed in Chapter 1, even though it is not
analytic in the second, different, and really less important sense.

Finally, we must note a difficult remaining question. What is there
to choose between understanding geometrical terms in a style that transforms geometrical sentences into empirical statements, and understanding geometrical terms in the style that transforms those same geometrical
sentences into a priori statements? Both viewpoints are possible; but
are both viewpoints equally plausible and advantageous? Here let us
recur to an example mentioned earlier: in the sixteenth- and seventeenth-
century dispute between those who said the earth moved and those who
said it was at rest, neither viewpoint was absurd. Each viewpoint could
accommodate the observed facts. Each viewpoint for its own justification could appeal to an actual tendency present in ordinary talk
about motion. Some people would go so far as to say that the dispute
was basically a verbal one and that both positions really were equally
correct. Yet to say that would be misleading and would be unfair to
the achievement of Copernicus, for there is reason to think that the
Copernican view was superior to the Ptolemaic view—the tendency in
ordinary talk about motion which the Copernican view emphasizes
is a deeper tendency than is the one which the Ptolemaic view emphasizes. This is why the transition from the Ptolemaic to the Copernican view represented such an important intellectual advance: it
enabled astronomers and physicists and everyone else to gain a clearer
grasp of what, in a sense, they had all along meant by motion; and at

the same time it led them to see that they had, in a sense, been mistaken in their heliocentric belief, and it thereby gave them a fresh and truer view of the solar system.

It may be the same with the twentieth-century choice between Euclidean and non-Euclidean geometry. Perhaps it could be held that those interpretations under which the sentences of geometry become empirical statements are interpretations which emphasize deeper and more important tendencies in our ordinary talk about space than does the sort of interpretation which makes the sentences of geometry into a priori statements. The layman is out of his depth here, but physicists at any rate seem markedly to prefer the point of view which interprets geometrical terms in ways that make the sentences of geometry into empirical statements. Physicists prefer to interpret Euclidean geometry so that it is false, rather than to say that gravity bends light rays and shrinks yardsticks. Physicists employ the geometry of Riemann in order to obtain a description of the universe which they find more manageable and more illuminating than is the description obtained by continuing to retain Euclidean principles.

We can at least say that this choice between interpreting geometry so that Euclidean laws of space may be retained or interpreting geometry so that Euclidean laws of space must be rejected, is an important linguistic choice of a kind that has occurred repeatedly in the history of thought. What is at stake is not a simple empirical question of truth and falsity, nor is the issue merely a verbal one; this is the kind of case where our problem is to decide which is the deeper of two conflicting tendencies, both present in our past use of the terms involved.

NUMBERS

AND LITERALISTIC PHILOSOPHIES

OF NUMBER

4

It has been customary ever since Euclid's time to present geometry in the form of an axiomatic system. Some other, different approaches to geometry have been developed by modern mathematicians, but this axiomatic approach has continued to be widely used and presented to beginners. Our mathematics of numbers, however, has not traditionally been organized in axiomatic form. Arithmetic, school algebra, and such subjects as the differential and integral calculus (which go under the heading of analysis) have customarily been presented as collections of rules of calculation, rather than in the form of axiomatized systems of laws. This difference is something of an historical accident. It arises from the fact that our modern mathematics of numbers has its origins more in the mathematics of the Babylonians, Hindus, and Arabs than in that of the Greeks. The Greeks did treat some numerical problems, to be sure, but in doing so their method was to give geometrical interpretations to numbers; that is, when dealing with a problem about the comparative size of two numbers, they would treat it as a problem about the comparative lengths of two lines or the comparative areas of two figures. But the Babylonians, Hindus, and Arabs (to whom we owe the word "algebra") gradually developed symbols and rules of calculation that made it possible to deal with numerical problems more abstractly and more powerfully than could the Greeks. As was typical in Eastern mathematics, however, the Babylonians, Hindus, and Arabs did not much concern themselves with giving proofs, let alone with organizing their knowledge of numbers into axiomatic form. Thus it happened that while geometry was being handed down through medieval and early modern times in the axiomatized form which Euclid had given it, the mathematics of number was passed along as a collection of comparatively unconnected laws and rules of calculation. This situation is finally changing; one of the striking features of twentieth-century mathematics is its greatly increased use of the axiomatic approach in mathematical studies besides geometry.

From very early times, the development of the mathematics of number must have given rise to philosophical puzzlement. The whole numbers, 1, 2, 3, etc., are not too disturbing, to be sure, for their legitimacy seems clear to us as we count the number of beasts in a herd or of kings in a dynasty. The fractions also are not too disturbing, for we can regard them as quotients of whole numbers, useful for comparing the sizes of fields or lengths of time. But one can imagine that there must have been a great stir of uneasiness when the Babylonians, wishing to be able to refer to the result of subtracting a number from itself, introduced a symbol for zero, and eventually began to treat it just as though zero were one of the whole numbers. Zero seems like an emptiness, like nothing; how then can we legitimately refer to zero as though it were something, a genuine number? No doubt this uneasiness was gradually soothed as people came to realize that zero is just right for 'counting' the number of beasts in an empty field, or the number of kings during a republican era. The introduction of symbols for negative numbers must have been a further source of uneasiness, however; negative numbers seem somehow to be numbers that are not there, unreal ghosts of numbers—so is it legitimate to call them numbers? In modern times the introduction of symbols for imaginary numbers excited similar qualms. Even if we admit the legitimacy of talk about negative numbers, is it not going much too far to speak of the square root of minus one as if it were a number? Wouldn't it be more honest just to say that minus one has no square root?

Philosophical puzzlement about the various kinds of numbers was much reduced thanks to the work of nineteenth-century mathematicians who developed a unified theory of numbers. Their very important achievement consisted in showing how the mathematical theories concerning more sophisticated kinds of numbers can be 'reduced to,' or 'constructed from,' a theory concerning only the basic kind of numbers. That is, they showed how each of the more sophisticated kinds of number, together with the operations (such as addition and multiplication) performable on numbers of that kind, can be *defined* in terms of the whole numbers and the operations performable upon them; and they showed that this can be done in such a way that the laws which govern these more sophisticated kinds of numbers can then be *deduced* from the laws that govern the whole numbers. This development is called the arithmetization of analysis, because it is concerned with showing how those parts of mathematics that go under the heading of analysis can be 'reduced' to the elementary part of arithmetic (or elementary number theory, as it is called), when that is supplemented by certain notions that we shall mention. This unified theory of numbers enables us to regard the various kinds of numbers as belonging to a single family, all springing from a single parent kind and all governed by laws that are strict deductive consequences of the laws governing that simple parent kind. If we accept this unified theory of numbers, we no longer need feel any special qualms about the more sophisticated kinds of number; any qualms that remain will be focused solely upon the numbers of the kind used in counting. Let us take a brief look at the sort of way in which one might 'reduce' these higher types of numbers.

The natural numbers   The numbers 0, 1, 2, 3, etc., will serve as our basic kind of numbers; they are called natural numbers (unfortunately that term has a slight ambiguity, for some writers include zero among the natural numbers while others do not—but let us count it in). Now, our intuitive idea of the natural numbers is that they are all those numbers each of which can be reached by starting from zero and adding one as often as necessary. The Italian mathematician Peano was the first to organize the fundamental laws of these numbers in axiomatic form; his set of five axioms is notable. Let us consider these axioms so that we can feel more at home with the natural numbers before we go on to see how other kinds of number can be reduced to them. Expressed in words, Peano's axioms are:

1. Zero is a natural number.
2. The immediate successor of any natural number is a natural number.
3. Distinct natural numbers never have the same immediate successor.
4. Zero is not the immediate successor of any natural number.
5. If something holds true of zero, and if, whenever it holds true of a natural number, it also holds true of the immediate successor of that natural number, then it holds true of all natural numbers.

These axioms contain three undefined terms: "zero," "immediate successor," and "natural number." The axioms by themselves do not show us what these terms are supposed to mean (though they do connect together whatever meanings these terms may have), nor do they give us any evidence that the terms do refer to anything real. If we wish to accept the axioms as true we must supply that understanding and that evidence for ourselves. Underlying the use of these terms in the axioms are the tacit assumptions that "zero" does refer to some one definite entity among those under discussion, and that for each entity among those under discussion there is just one entity among them that is its immediate successor. It follows from the axioms that the immediate successor of zero, its immediate successor, and so on and on, all are natural numbers; and (by the fifth axiom) that nothing else is a natural number. From the axioms it follows that there must be infinitely many natural numbers, since the series cannot stop, nor can it circle back to its starting point (because zero is not the immediate successor of any natural number). The fifth axiom is especially important, for it expresses the assumption which underlies mathematical induction (this has nothing to do with inductive reasoning as discussed in the first chapter, but is an important form of deductive mathematical reasoning). We can picture how reasoning by mathematical induction works if we imagine a series of dominoes standing in a row: suppose we know that the first domino will fall and that whenever any domino falls the adjoining one also will fall; then we are entitled to infer that all the dominoes will fall, no matter how many there may be. In the same spirit, if we know that something holds true of zero and that whenever it holds true of a natural number it also holds true of the immediate successor of that natural number, then we can infer that it holds true of every natural number. On the basis of Peano's axioms, we can introduce the names of further numbers: "one" by definition names the immediate successor of zero, "two" by definition names the immediate successor of one, and so on.

Peano's axioms express in a very clear way the essential principles about the natural numbers. However, they do not by themselves constitute a sufficient basis to permit the 'reduction' of other higher kinds of numbers—assuming, that is, that we continue to restrict ourselves to the same comparatively low-level logical principles that are employed for deducing theorems in geometry. There are two reasons for this. For one thing, Peano's axioms do not by themselves provide us even with a complete theory of the natural numbers. If we limit ourselves just to Peano's three primitive terms and to his five axioms, it is impossible for us (using only normal low-level logical principles) to define addition and multiplication in their general sense for these numbers; and so we could not even express within the system, let alone prove within it, such laws as that the sum of natural numbers x and y always is the same number as the sum of y and x, or that x times the sum of y and z always is the same number as the sum of x times y and x times z. (We do not even worry about subtraction and division, since these are not operations freely performable on the natural numbers.) Furthermore, in order to carry out this reduction of higher kinds of number we need to employ two other very important terms, "set" and "ordered pair," which Peano of course did not include among his primitives (and which do not belong to normal low-level logic). Let us take a moment to discuss how these two terms are to be understood.

For our purposes, the terms "set" and "ordered pair" must be understood in a rather rarefied way. A set is a class, collection, or group of things; the things belonging to a set may be of any kind, concrete or abstract, and they may or may not be closely similar or closely connected with one another. The one essential point is that a set has to be thought of as a single entity, and has to be distinguished from the things that are members of it. Consider the set of philosophers, that is, the set whose members include every philosopher but nothing else. This set is very different from any of its members: each member is a philosopher, but the set of all philosophers definitely is not itself a philosopher; the set is numerous (it has many members) but no philosopher is numerous. Thus, the set must be distinguished from its members. Two sets are said to be identical when and only when they have exactly the same members; thus, for example, the set of equilateral triangles is identical to the set of equiangular triangles. We do allow ourselves to speak of an empty set, a set having no members; but in light of this criterion of identity all empty sets are identical, and there can be only one empty set. Thus, the set of unicorns is identical to the set of square circles, since these sets have exactly the same members—none. One set is a subset of another when all the members of the former are members of the latter; thus the set of philosophers is a subset of the set of humans. We must be sure to distinguish between a subset and a member, however: Plato is a member but not a subset of the set of philosophers, while the set of philosophers is a subset but not a member of the set of humans.

The term "ordered pair" has to be understood in a similarly rarefied sense. An ordered pair consists of two things of any kind whatever, considered in a certain order. The things may be concrete or abstract, similar or dissimilar. One ordered pair $x;y$ is said to be identical with another ordered pair $z;w$ if and only if the two first items are identical (x is identical with z) and the two second items are identical as well (y is identical with w). It is possible to define ordered pairs as a certain kind of sets of sets, but that is a refinement which we shall pass over.

Let us now imagine that we possess an axiomatic system in which can be expressed and proved all the fundamental laws of the natural numbers, and in which we can express and prove the fundamental laws governing sets and ordered pairs. This is the basis that we need for 'reducing' the higher kinds of numbers.

The procedure of reducing the higher kinds of numbers to the natural numbers is carried out in a series of steps. First we develop a theory of the rational numbers, basing it entirely upon our theory of natural numbers, sets, and ordered pairs. Then we develop a theory of the real numbers, basing it upon our theory of the rationals. Then we move on to the signed real numbers, then to the complex numbers. At each step, we take for granted that it is understood what the preceding kind of numbers are and, equally important, what it means to add and to multiply them. On this basis we define what the next kind of numbers are, and we define what it shall mean to add and to multiply them. When we have finally expanded the domain of number to include all these kinds of numbers, we can then see how complex numbers—the farthest removed from natural ones—can be reduced to natural numbers, since we have explained the rational in terms of the natural numbers, the real in terms of the rational, and the complex in terms of the signed real numbers.

Let us start with the rational numbers. These we intuitively think of as the numbers that can be represented as fractions having natural numbers for numerator and denominator. We remember from school arithmetic that x/y equals z/w when and only when $x \times w$ equals $z \times y$. By analogy with that, we can arbitrarily introduce the term "equals" for speaking about ordered pairs of natural numbers. Where x, y, z, w are natural numbers, let us say that the ordered pair $x;y$ equals the ordered pair $z;w$ if and only if neither y nor w is zero and the natural number $x \times w$ is identical to the natural number $z \times y$. (Notice here that two ordered pairs could be equal without being identical.) Now we are in a position to offer a definition of rational numbers. We can define a rational number as any non-empty set of ordered pairs of natural numbers such that each ordered pair in the set is equal to every other in it and any equal to one in it is in it too.

We must also define what we shall mean by adding rational numbers. We get a hint of how the definition can go if we recall from school arithmetic that

$$\frac{x_1}{y_1} + \frac{x_2}{y_2} = \frac{(x_1 \times y_2) + (x_2 \times y_1)}{y_1 \times y_2}$$

Let us now consider any three rational numbers R_1, R_2, and R_3, where $x_1;y_1$ is an ordered pair of natural numbers belonging to R_1, and $x_2;y_2$ is an ordered pair of natural numbers belonging to R_2, and $x_3;y_3$ is an ordered pair of natural numbers belonging to R_3. By analogy with the rule of school arithmetic, we can now say that R_3 shall be called the sum of R_1 and R_2 if and only if $x_3;y_3$ equals the ordered pair $([x_1 \times y_2] + [x_2 \times y_1]);(y_1 \times y_2)$. Assuming that we understand what it is to add and multiply natural numbers, this definition tells us what it shall mean to add rational numbers. The definition is designed to ensure that two rational numbers always do have a rational number as their sum, and that addition shall have its familiar properties (such as that $R_1 + R_2$ is identical to $R_2 + R_1$). Multiplication of rationals can be defined in a rather parallel fashion.

Next we come to the real numbers. Intuitively one might think of a real number as any number that can be used for comparing one length or area with another. Thus $\sqrt{2}$ is the number we need for comparing the length of the hypotenuse with that of the side of an isosceles right triangle—yet there is no such rational number as this, as the Greeks proved, to their dismay. We can develop a conception of the real numbers if we think of the rational numbers as arranged in order of increasing magnitude from left to right like points on a line (the series is 'dense' in the sense that between every two rationals there are other rationals). Now we can picture a 'cut' being made in this series. (The notion of a 'cut' comes from the German mathematician Dedekind.) Let us suppose the 'cut' is made in such a way that among those rationals to the left of the 'cut' no one of them is the largest (whichever one you pick, there are others that are larger). Then we can consider the set of all rationals lying to the left of the 'cut,' and that set will have these three features: (i) not all the rationals belong to it; (ii) it has no largest member; (iii) every rational belonging to the set is smaller than any rational not belonging to it. Such a set we shall call a real number. Under this definition, a real number is a special kind of set of rationals; that is (in light of our definition of rational numbers), a real number is a kind of set of sets of ordered pairs of natural numbers. Thus, for example, the real number $\sqrt{2}$ is the set containing all and only those rationals whose squares are rationals smaller than two.

We can define what addition shall mean for real numbers by saying that real numbers X and Y have the real number Z as their sum if and only if when any rational belonging to X is added to any rational belonging to Y their sum is a rational belonging to Z. This definition is constructed so as to ensure that every two real numbers do have a unique real number as their sum, and that the familiar laws of addition hold. Multiplication of real numbers can be defined in a parallel fashion.

The signed numbers—that is, the positive and negative real numbers—can then be defined as a certain kind of sets of ordered pairs of real numbers. And the complex numbers—those having imaginary components involving the square root of minus one—can be defined as a certain sort of sets of ordered pairs of signed numbers.

It is important to notice in connection with this hierarchy of numbers that the name "one," for instance, has several different meanings. It appears first as the name of a natural number (the immediate successor of zero). Then it appears as the name of a rational number (a rational number is a set of ordered pairs of natural numbers, and the rational number one is the set containing the ordered pairs 1;1 and 2;2 and 3;3 and all the innumerable other ordered pairs of natural numbers 'equal' to these). Then it appears as the name of a real number (a real number is a set of rationals, and the real number one is the set of all those innumerably many rationals smaller than the rational number one). We must distinguish between the natural number one, the rational number one, the real number one, and so on. Ordinarily the same numeral is used to stand for all of these, but they are essentially distinct mathematical entities.

This development that we have just sketched, or hinted at, aims to show how all the higher types of numbers and the operations upon them can be defined in terms of the natural numbers and their operations. And it aims at constructing these definitions so that the laws of these higher types of numbers can be deduced from the basic laws that govern the natural numbers. On account of this, the German mathematician Kronecker uttered the often quoted remark, "Dear God made the whole numbers, all the others are human work." The development is of philosophical importance not only as an example of mathematical thinking, but because it shows that if we accept these reductions, then all our philosophical puzzlement and concern about numbers can be focused solely upon the natural numbers and their laws, together with sets and ordered pairs and their laws.

Transfinite numbers   In developing definitions of the higher kinds of numbers we have made use of the term "set." The idea of developing a theory of sets and treating it as a special subject in its own right goes back to the German mathematician Cantor in the late nineteenth century. Cantor's particular contribution was his theory of infinite sets and of transfinite numbers. It can be regarded as a further extension of the development we were considering in the preceding section.

Cantor's theory employs the important notion of one-to-one correspondence. We say that the members of one set S_1 stand in one-to-one correspondence with the members of another set S_2 provided there is some way of associating members of the one set with those of the other so that with each member of S_1 exactly one member of S_2 is associated, and with each member of S_2 exactly one member of S_1 is associated. Consider passengers in a bus: if every seat is occupied by one passenger and if every passenger occupies one seat, then the set of passengers and the set of seats are in one-to-one correlation. Under these circumstances the set of passengers would of course have the same number of members as has the set of seats, no matter how many of each there were. On the other hand, if every seat were occupied by a passenger but some passengers had no seats, then the set of passengers would be larger than the set of seats. In this example we have considered two sets of finite size (there could not be an infinitely large bus). Cantor's notion was that the members of infinitely large sets can stand in one-to-one correlation too, so that the sizes of sets may be compared even when they contain infinitely many members. He held that two infinite sets should be said to have the same size if and only if their members can be correlated one-to-one; and that one infinite set is larger than another if and only if when all the members of the latter are associated with members of the former then always there are some members of the former left over. Thus, for example, the set of odd numbers and the set of even numbers are the same size, for we can correlate their members one-to-one, each odd number being associated with its immediate successor.

We are not surprised that according to Cantor's definition of sameness of size the set of odd numbers and the set of even numbers are the same size. But it is surprising that according to his definition the set of natural numbers and the set of odd numbers also turn out to be the same size. Here the point is that there is a way of correlating the members of these two sets one-to-one:

Odd numbers	1	3	5	7	9	11	. . .
Natural numbers	0	1	2	3	4	5	. . .

What we do is to associate the first odd number with the first natural number, and in general the nth odd number with the nth natural number; and this is a one-to-one correlation.

Still more surprising is that the set of natural numbers turns out to be the same size as the set of rational numbers, which we might have imagined would be much larger. To show that this is so, we must arrange the rational numbers in a series so that every rational number has its definite place in the series and so that each is within a finite number of steps of the beginning of the series. Then we shall be able to correlate the first rational with the first natural number, and in general the nth rational with the nth natural number. Suppose we express each rational as a fraction. Consider the array:

$$
\begin{array}{cccc}
0/1 & 1/1 & 2/1 & 3/1 \ldots \\
0/2 & 1/2 & 2/2 & 3/2 \ldots \\
0/3 & 1/3 & 2/3 & 3/3 \ldots \\
\cdot & \cdot & \cdot & \cdot \\
\cdot & \cdot & \cdot & \cdot \\
\cdot & \cdot & \cdot & \cdot
\end{array}
$$

If we think of this array as continuing to the right and downwards without ever stopping, then every rational number must occur in the array. The array is two-dimensional, but we can arrange all its members in a linear series if we start at the upper left corner and weave diagonally through the array. The series we get goes:

$$0/1, \ 1/1, \ 0/2, \ 0/3, \ 1/2, \ 2/1, \ 3/1, \ 2/2, \ 1/3 \ldots$$

This series contains some repetions of rational numbers (0/2 and 0/3 are the same number as 0/1, for instance), so let us remove from the series any member that has already occurred in it. This now gives us a series in which every rational number occurs exactly once, and each member of the series is within a finite number of steps of the beginning.

Rational numbers	0/1,	1/1,	1/2,	2/1,	3/1,	1/3 $\ldots$
Natural numbers	0,	1,	2,	3,	4,	5 $\ldots$

Thus we have a one-to-one correlation between the members of the set of rational numbers and the members of the set of natural numbers; and hence these two sets are the same size.

That the odd numbers, which form only a subset of the natural numbers, are just as numerous as the natural numbers, and that the natural numbers are just as numerous as the rational numbers are findings which seem to contradict Euclid's axiom, "The whole is greater than any of its parts." Does this show that Euclid's axiom was mistaken? That is a delicate question, a question rather like the question whether Ptolemaic astronomers were mistaken in believing that the earth does not move. Euclid, in enunciating his axiom, of course was thinking only of finite wholes; the Greeks never discussed infinite wholes. If Cantor's theory had been made known to Euclid, perhaps Euclid would have accepted it, saying, "My mistake. I failed to think about infinite wholes." On the other hand, perhaps Euclid would have rejected it, saying, "To talk about infinite 'wholes' of the 'same size' is to misuse language. If Cantor wants to express his theory in a way that will not be necessarily false, then he should talk about infinite *smoles* having the same *smize*." Which answer would Euclid be better justified in giving? The matter is well worth reflecting upon, but it is not easy to reach a clear-cut conclusion. At any rate, we can recognize that Cantor's theory emphasizes certain tendencies, but neglects other tendencies latent in the previous use of the terms "whole" and "same size."

Cantor's surprising result concerning the set of rational numbers might lead us to suppose that, according to his theory, perhaps all infinite sets are the same size. Cantor argued that this is not so, however. To simplify matters, let us consider just the real numbers that are greater than zero but not greater than one. Cantor maintained that there are more of these real numbers than there are natural numbers. To establish this conclusion he argued indirectly by *reductio ad absurdum*. Suppose the set of these real numbers were the same size as the set of all natural numbers. That would mean that these real numbers could somehow all be arranged in a series (call it $r_1, r_2, r_3, \ldots r_n \ldots$) so that the first real number in that series could be correlated with the first natural number in the series of natural numbers, and the nth real number could be correlated with the nth natural number. Now, each of these real numbers can be represented in decimal notation as a nonterminating decimal (a nonterminating decimal is one that never reaches a place after which all the digits are "0"). Some of these real numbers would have to be expressed as nonterminating decimals anyway: thus, $1/3$ is $.33333\ldots$ Others that would terminate can be put into nonterminating form: thus $.303$ can be expressed as $.3029999\ldots$ But now consider the real number (let us call it "r_0") represented by the following nonterminating decimal: its first digit is to be "5" if the first digit of r_1 is not "5" and is to be "6" otherwise; its second digit is to be "5" if the second digit of r_2 is not "5" and is to be "6" otherwise; and in general its nth digit is to be "5" if the nth digit of r_n is not "5" and is to be "6" otherwise. This nonterminating decimal must represent a real number greater than zero but not greater than one, yet this real number r_0 is so defined that it cannot be identical with any real number in the series $r_1, r_2, r_3 \ldots r_n \ldots$ Thus this real number r_0 has not been correlated with any natural number. This contradicts our supposition that a one-to-one correlation between these real numbers and the natural numbers was possible. Therefore, such a one-to-one correlation is not possible, and there are more of these real numbers than there are natural numbers. The set of real numbers is larger than the set of rationals.

Cantor went on to develop a theory of transfinite cardinal numbers. A cardinal number measures the size of a set, finite or infinite; transfinite cardinals measure the sizes of infinite sets, which we have been discussing. The set of natural numbers has the smallest transfinite cardinal number; the set of real numbers has, as we have seen, a larger transfinite cardinal number; but the set of all subsets of the set of real numbers has an even larger transfinite cardinal number. Cantor arrived at the latter conclusion by reasoning similar to what we have just been through. He said that every non-empty set, whether finite or infinite, has more subsets than it contains members. This means that the cardinal number of the set of subsets of a given non-empty set must always be larger than the cardinal number of the given set. And this guarantees that no matter how large a cardinal number may be, there are other cardinal numbers larger still. Thus Cantor held that there are infinitely many different cardinal numbers, which can be arranged in an ascending sequence.

Cantor's surprising conclusions can be regarded as a natural outgrowth of the development discussed in the preceding section. We can think of Cantor's results being established as theorems in the axiomatic system which we imagined earlier: a system whose axioms express the basic laws of the natural numbers and of sets and ordered pairs. Around the turn of the century, many mathematicians had the exhilarating conviction that it should in principle be possible for one single axiomatic system of this kind to be developed that would embrace all kinds of numbers finite and transfinite, and that would yield all the traditional branches of mathematics (geometry being treated through numerical interpretations, as analytic geometry does). Much had already been achieved in this direction, and their hope was that before long one single comprehensive axiomatic system of mathematics could be worked out. In the next chapter we shall consider what became of this hope.

Should we try to interpret number theory? The majority of mathematicians have been content to work with the natural numbers without devoting much attention to what the term "natural number" means or to whether we have reason to believe that there really are such entities. They have been content to follow out the logical consequences of initial assumptions such as those embodied in Peano's axioms, feeling that mathematics fully accomplishes its proper task when it establishes that its theorems are deducible from its axioms. Some people would even go so far as to say, "It's absurd for muddled laymen and philosophers to wonder what numbers are or whether they exist; pure mathematics is entirely hypothetical, in this sense: all we care about is that *if* certain axioms are true *then* it is logically necessary that certain theorems be true as well. Your questions of meaning and existence are utterly irrelevant to pure mathematics." The point of view is partly justified; certainly the mathematics of number can fruitfully be pursued without any consideration of the nature or existence of the basic numbers. An axiomatized theory of the natural numbers can be regarded as an uninterpreted system and can be investigated in an abstract logical manner. However, this point of view surely goes too far when it attempts to prohibit reflection about the nature and existence of numbers.

The intellectual significance of number theory as a body of knowledge depends not merely upon whether it forms an interesting and logically consistent system. It also depends upon whether there is any important sense in which the axioms of number theory are true. Now, a subject such as Lobachevskian geometry is of intellectual interest and deserves study, even if we always study it only as an uninterpreted system—that is, even if we never find any scientifically important interpretation of its primitive terms under which its axioms all come out true. Its intellectual significance would be heightened, however, if we could find some important interpretation under which the system did come out true. Unlike Lobachevskian geometry, the theory of numbers is widely and continually used both in everyday life and in science. It therefore seems plausible to suppose that there may be some important interpretation under which the theory of numbers comes out true. Perhaps not the only way, but at least the most straightforward way of explaining why in science and in everyday life it is so useful to apply the theory of numbers, would be by showing that the theory has some especially important interpretation under which its laws become truths that have value as premises for scientific and for everyday reasoning.

This point becomes especially sharp in connection with Cantor's transfinite numbers. Many thinkers, including such prominent philosophers as Aristotle and Kant, have believed that there cannot be an actually infinite number of things in the universe. In saying this, they surely meant to be using the word "number" in an important everyday sense. And they were somehow denying what Cantor says in this theory of transfinite numbers, when he formulates the principle that there is a hierarchy of ever larger and larger infinite sets. But of course what Aristotle and Kant were saying cannot be the denial of what Cantor says unless both sides attach some sense to the term "number," and indeed attach substantially the same sense to it. Cantor and other mathematicians who agreed with him surely were not using "cardinal number" merely as an uninterpreted term: they, too, understood Cantor's laws as specific assertions, and they thought them true rather than false. Possibly they were all talking confused nonsense; but certainly we are not entitled to dismiss their talk as nonsensical unless we first make a strenuous effort to see what sense it might have.

In the remainder of this chapter we shall briefly consider three main points of view which hold that there is some literal interpretation of number theory under which its axioms will come out true. To the question, "Do numbers exist?" these viewpoints do not offer figurative answers such as "Yes, of course, in the sense that the term 'number' occurs in theorems deduced from axioms," or "Yes, of course, in the sense that talk about numbers proves fruitful for science." Instead they try to hold that things deserving the name of numbers, things for which the laws of mathematics hold true, do literally exist. To hold that such things 'literally exist' is to hold that they are in no sense imaginary or fictional. It is to hold that they should be said to exist in the same logical tone of voice in which we speak of the existence of whatever we think of as being really real (whether that be physical objects, sense data, or the Absolute).

The problem of trying to find a literal interpretation of number theory is rather analogous to the problem of 'universals' which pre-occupied medieval philosophy. The problem of universals was a problem about the status of properties, such as virtue, squareness, and redness. We perhaps find instances of virtue in the world, but virtue itself seems not to be a thing that is located in space or time; yet we speak of it as though it were something, and we profess to have knowledge of it. Virtue, squareness, redness, and all other such universals appear to be abstract entities; that is, things not located either in space or time. What reality do these universals possess? Their status seems very puzzling and mysterious. If they are intangible, immaterial entities, how then can we have knowledge of them, and how can they be so important in our thinking? Philosophical answers to this medieval problem fell under three headings. Realists maintained that universals were real abstract entities, at least as real as concrete objects, and that the mind has the power to discover and comprehend them by means of rational insight. Conceptualists maintained that though universals are real abstract entities, they do not have any reality in the world apart from our thinking—they are created within the mind. Nominalists maintained that either there are no such things as universals or they are not abstract entities.

As regards number theory, our problem has to do with the reality of the natural numbers (and of sets and ordered pairs) rather than with the reality of properties. But numbers, like properties, appear to be abstract rather than concrete entities—that is, things not located in space or time. This is what makes the medieval question parallel to this one about mathematics. Because the two questions are rather parallel, the answers that modern thinkers have given to the question about numbers can be classified under three headings parallel to the three medieval headings. We may classify as nominalists those who hold that numbers are not abstract entities and that if there is any way of interpreting number theory so as to make it true this must be done by reference to concrete objects. We may classify as conceptualists those who hold that there are numbers and that they are abstract entities, but that they are creations of the mind. And we may classify as realists those who hold without qualm that numbers as abstract entities literally exist independently of our thinking.

Nominalism   Nominalism is the general view that there are no abstract entities, and more specifically it is the view that there are no abstract entities that can be identified as numbers. Is it then possible for a nominalist to hold that there are ways of interpreting number theory so as to make it come out true? Can he maintain that when the mathematics of number appears to be talking about abstract entities it is not really doing so; that it can be interpreted as talking about things the existence of which nominalism can accept? Let us consider some possible nominalistic lines of thought.

Many people, when asked what numbers are, will reply that numbers are ideas in our minds. This line of thought always seems attractive to people confronted with philosophical problems about the existence of something problematic. Suppose that an 'idea' here is understood as being a mental image or some such mental phenomenon in the mind of an individual thinker. An 'idea' of this sort would be something that comes into being at a particular time, lasts for a while, then ceases to exist. It would be definitely located in time, even if not in space, and so would not be an abstract entity in our sense. Thus the view that numbers are ideas of this sort must be classified as a form of nominalism (even though it resembles conceptualism in connecting numbers with the mind).

The suggestion that numbers are ideas in the mind comes very readily to people's lips, but it is not a very satisfactory view. As an attempt to provide an interpretation under which number theory will come out true, this view is defective in several ways. For one thing, number theory holds that there is just one natural number that is zero; yet if numbers were ideas in this sense then there would be as many different numbers that are zero as there are people who have ideas of zero. Also, number theory maintains that every natural number has an immediate successor; but in all probability there are natural numbers (large ones) such that no person has ever formed ideas of their immediate successors. Thus, the view that numbers are ideas entails that, contrary to what number theory claims, there do not exist immediate successors of these large natural numbers. Moreover, number theory cannot be true unless there are infinitely many natural numbers; and it is doubtful, perhaps even senseless, to claim that people possess infinitely many number-ideas in their minds. We must conclude that this line of thought, according to which numbers are ideas, fails to provide any interpretation of number theory under which its axioms and theorems can all come out true.

Another nominalistic line of thought appeals to physical rather than to mental entities. We ordinarily distinguish between numbers and numerals; a numeral is a mark having a certain shape which we think of as being the name of a number. Thus the arabic numeral "5" and the roman numeral "V" are both ordinarily regarded as names for the number five. But suppose we were just to identify numbers with numerals; suppose we say that the numbers are nothing over and above the numerals. This seems to make the numbers into something definite and perceptible; there can be no doubt but that there exist numerals, for we see them. By identifying numbers with numerals it may seem that we rid mathematics of its dependence upon abstract entities.

This nominalistic line of thought is no more satisfactory than the preceding one, however. Under this kind of interpretation the axioms of number theory again do not come out literally true. For example, number theory says that each natural number has exactly one immediate successor; but if numbers were numerals this would not hold true. If by a numeral we mean a particular mark actually written on a piece of paper, on an athlete's uniform, or the like, then there are enormously many numerals for the smaller numbers—but no numerals at all for the very large numbers which no one has ever specifically referred to in writing.

If the numerals won't do, then perhaps the nominalist could just identify each natural number with some particular object in the physical world. Suppose he somehow arranges his interpretation of the primitive terms of number theory so that the symbol "0" is understood as referring to the Peak of Tenerife, "1" as referring to Popocatapetl, "2" as referring to Chacaltaya, and so on. Would something along this line do as a nominalistic interpretation of number theory? No, for infinitely many objects would be required; but there are not that many mountains on earth, nor could we have any assurance that there are that many objects of any kind, even electrons, in the whole universe. We never succeed in observing more than a finite number of objects of any kind; inductive reasoning, based on evidence drawn from our observations, never could establish as probable any conclusion to the effect that there actually exist an infinite number of things of any observable type.

Furthermore, these nominalistic suggestions regarding numbers do not offer any hint as to how the terms "set" and "ordered pair" are to be interpreted nominalistically. A supposed nominalist would not be very consistent if he refused to admit that the natural numbers could be abstract entities, yet did not object to talking about sets of natural numbers (as must be done if we are to define the rationals as sets of ordered pairs of natural numbers). On the face of it, a set (which must be distinguished from its members) appears to be an abstract entity if it is anything at all. It is possible to overlook this if one speaks about a set as an 'aggregate' or a 'collection,' thus making a set of silverware sound like the same thing as a pile of silverware. The pile is indeed a concrete thing located in space and time; it is as concrete as the knives, forks, and spoons that go together to compose it. But the set of silverware cannot be identified with the pile of silverware, for a pile of forty-eight pieces can be identical with a pile of eight place-settings; yet the set of pieces of silverware cannot be identical with the set of place-settings, since these two sets are of different sizes, the former having forty-eight and the latter only eight members. Parallel remarks can be made about ordered pairs.

It seems impossible to avoid the conclusion that number theory cannot be given any thoroughly nominalistic interpretation under which it will come out literally true. The convinced nominalist will have to view the system of number theory as incapable of having any true interpretation. Of course, to say that the axioms and theorems of the mathematics of number are incapable of truth would not necessarily be to deny that they may be useful; false and even senseless talk may sometimes be very helpful in carrying us along through life—in getting bridges built or elections won. For the convinced nominalist, however, the mathematics of number ought not to be regarded as a body of literal knowledge. Some non-nominalists would regard this conclusion as a *reductio ad absurdum* of nominalism.

Conceptualism and the intuitionists   The view that mathematical objects such as numbers and sets are creatures of the mind, abstract entities brought into being by thinking, is a view that many people have found attractive. It seems to preserve a kind of reality for these entities, while still hard-headedly conceding that they have no independent existence. Moreover, it is a view having a certain charm, for it accords extraordinary dignity to the activity of the mathematician. Indeed, an extreme form of conceptualism would hold that the mind has the power of creating whatever numbers or other mathematical entities it pleases in a perfectly free and omnipotent manner. The mathematician's postulates then could be picturesquely compared to the creative fiats of the Deity: when the mathematician thinks to himself, "Let it be postulated that there are numbers of such-and-such a kind," he thereby brings them into being, his sovereign creative power being like that of an omnipotent Deity who creates out of nothing whatever He wills to be.

It would be too extreme, however, to imagine that the mathematician is entirely free of restrictions in this activity. One cannot compare the mathematician to the creative Deity as described by voluntaristic theologians, who suppose Him to be subject to no restrictions whatsoever (so powerful that He could turn a harlot into a virgin, to use one of the traditional examples). Whatever may or may not hold as regards the Deity, mathematicians at any rate are subject to the requirements of consistency, and cannot bring into being self-contradictions. For example, suppose someone attempts to postulate the existence of an entity answering to the description "A natural number which is the cardinal number of the set of natural numbers." It might at first sight appear that this is a perfectly good description, and that a mathematician could postulate such an entity if he likes. Yet if someone tries to join the assumption that there is such a thing to the normal axioms for the natural numbers, inconsistency results (for if there were a natural number that was the cardinal number of the set of natural numbers, it would have to be both finite and not finite, which is a contradiction). An attempted creative fiat like this would be unsuccessful at bringing its 'object' into being. This instance must serve as a warning that not everyone who imagines himself to have created something has succeeded in doing so. The conceptualist who supposes that thinking can bring numbers into being must at any rate grant that in this game of creation there is a difference between the wish and its execution. Moreover, the principal thinkers who have advocated this conceptualistic view have held that the human mind's creative powers are rather narrowly limited, limited by even more than the requirements of formal logical consistency.

It is the philosopher Kant who was historically the most important representative of a conceptualistic view regarding the mathematics of number. Kant held that the laws of number, like the laws of Euclidean geometry, are both a priori and synthetic. Although Kant did not express his view concerning the philosophy of number in quite as explicit a form as he did his view concerning the philosophy of space, he did say enough to leave his readers with the impression that for him our knowledge of number rests upon an awareness of time as a 'pure form of intuition' and upon awareness by the mind of its own capacity to repeat the act of counting, time after time. This is his explanation of how such synthetic a priori knowledge is possible: in knowing the laws of number the mind is gaining insight only into its own inner workings, not into reality as it is in itself. Of course this is parallel to Kant's view that our synthetic a priori knowledge of Euclidean geometry rests upon awareness of space as a 'form of intuition' and upon the mind's awareness of its own capacity to construct spatial figures in pure imagination. Kant actually says that it is through synthetic a priori insight that we know particular facts about numbers, such as that 5 plus 7 equals 12. This is not very plausible, for particular facts like this, especially ones regarding the larger numbers, surely can and often must be proved. What we might better consider is the view that the basic axioms of number theory should be understood and justified according to Kant's philosophy.

Now, apparently Kant's conception of arithmetic as based on the intuition of counting means that numbers exist if and only if they can be reached by counting; and presumably he would have wanted to say that sets exist if and only if their members can be counted. In consequence, there will be no definitely largest number, since one can always count beyond any number up to which one has counted. But there cannot be any infinite numbers (transfinite numbers) either, since to count infinitely high would be impossible (it would require an infinite length of time, Kant thinks—more than we have available). Similarly, Kant holds that in geometry there is no maximum length of line, for we can imagine extending further any line already drawn; but there cannot be an infinitely long line, as we cannot draw a line that long in imagination (to do so would require infinite time). Thus, both with numbers and with lines, Kant is committed to a doctrine of what is called the *potential* infinite, or of *indefinite* totalities, rather than to the doctrine of the *actual* infinite. Kant's stand is made use of by him elsewhere in his philosophy when he argues that certain unsolvable contradictions (which he calls the antinomies) arise if one argues on the assumption that the spatio-temporal universe could contain any actually infinite totalities. Aristotle, too, had used a somewhat similar notion of the potential infinite in his treatment of philosophical problems, such as Zeno's famous paradoxes of motion.

In recent times a group of mathematicians, among whom the Dutchman Brouwer has been the central figure, have given new currency to a philosophy of mathematics derived from Kant's. Brouwer, like Kant, has maintained that a 'pure intuition' of temporal counting serves as the point of departure for the mathematics of number; and for this reason the name "intuitionism" has been given to the philosophy of this group. For these modern mathematicians, however, intuitionism has not just been a philosophical theory as it was for Kant; for them it has also been a view permeating their actual mathematical work, to such an extent that their judgments about the validity of mathematical arguments have differed from the judgments of other mathematicians who do not accept intuitionism.

Specifically, an argument such as Cantor's argument that there are more real numbers than there are natural numbers is not accepted as valid by intuitionists, although many other mathematicians have regarded it as valid. In carrying out that proof Cantor defined a certain real number (we called it r_0) by saying that in its nonterminating decimal representation its nth digit is to be "5" if the nth digit of r_n is not "5"; otherwise it is to be "6." An intuitionist cannot regard this definition as legitimate, for the definition does not show us how to 'construct' this real number through our pure intuitive activity of counting and calculating. The definition gives us a rule, but to apply the rule and 'create' this real number we would have to complete an infinite number of steps, running through every single digit of the real number; and we have not time for that, the intuitionist holds. Thus he rejects as invalid Cantor's argument that there are more real than natural numbers, and with it he rejects Cantor's whole theory of transfinite numbers.

Cantor's proof is 'non-constructive.' That is, it requires us to envisage the completing of a task involving an infinite number of steps. Now, it might be objected that ordinary reasoning by mathematical induction also seems in a sense to envisage the completing of an infinite number of steps. In ordinary reasoning by mathematical induction, knowing that something holds of zero and that it holds of the successor of each natural number of which it holds, we infer that it holds of all natural numbers. Here, are we entitled to reach the conclusion that whatever-it-is holds for all natural numbers, if we cannot envisage ourselves completing the task of running through all of them? Does the intuitionist reject mathematical induction? The answer is that he need not do so. For our conclusion to the effect that something holds for all the natural numbers is a conclusion that need not be understood as claiming that we have run through the infinite series of natural numbers. Instead, it may be regarded as saying that for any particular natural number you choose, we can count from zero up to it and thus can show that the requirement, whatever it is, holds true of it. Looked at in this way, the reasoning is 'constructive,' since each particular natural number can be reached by running through only a finite number of steps of counting.

From the point of view of intuitionism, we must possess a constructive proof of any mathematical statement about numbers before we are entitled to say that we know the statement is true. If the statement asserts the existence of at least one number of such-and-such a kind, then we must know how to construct, or compute, such a number, using only a finite number of steps. Or if the statement asserts that all numbers are of such-and-such a kind, then for any given number we must be able to demonstrate, using only a finite number of steps, that it is of the given kind. Similarly, before we are entitled to say that we know a statement to be false, we must possess a constructive disproof of it. What about cases in which we so far possess neither a proof nor a disproof of a mathematical statement?

Two well-known examples of mathematical assertions that have neither been proved nor disproved deserve mention. Fermat's so-called 'last theorem' asserts that there do not exist natural numbers which satisfy the equation: $x^n + y^n = z^n$ for n greater than 2. 'Goldbach's conjecture' asserts that every even number can be expressed as the sum of two prime numbers (where a prime number is a number not evenly divisible by any whole number except 1 and itself). Despite a great deal of effort, mathematicians have been unable to find proofs of either of these assertions; nor have they succeeded in disproving them. We have no assurance that they ever will succeed in doing either thing.

Now, the intuitionist takes a radical line with regard to examples such as these. The intuitionist believes that numbers are creatures of the mind, and he believes with Kant that whatever the mind creates it must in principle be able to know through and through. He holds that there can be no unknowable (that is, not constructively provable) truth or falsity about numbers. Therefore, he maintains that we have no assurance that Fermat's last theorem and Goldbach's conjecture are either true or false. If they can neither be proved nor disproved, then they are neither true nor false. We cannot prove that they can neither be proved nor disproved (and so possess neither truth nor falsity), but it may well be so, the intuitionist thinks. Intuitionism thus rejects the law of the 'excluded middle'—the principle of traditional logic that every statement is either true or false and that there is no middle possibility. The intuitionist does recognize a middle possibility, and holds that there may well be meaningful statements possessing neither truth nor falsity.[1]

It is clear then, that the intuitionist has a more puritanical standard of logical rigor than had mathematicians such as Cantor. All reasoning acceptable to the former is acceptable to the latter, but (as we saw) some reasoning acceptable to the latter is not acceptable to the former. Now, if Cantor's theory of the transfinite were the only thing in mathematics whose sacrifice was demanded by the intuitionist's scrupulous standards, then perhaps no one would mind very much. We could do without Cantor's theory without feeling any great sense of deprivation. However, there are some important elements of more classical mathematics whose sacrifice the intuitionist's scruples also demand. One important victim would be the theorem in analysis that every bounded set of real numbers has a least upper bound. Intuitionism cannot accept this, because to define the real number that is the least upper bound of a set of real numbers requires a definition that must mention a set to which the thing being defined may belong (such definitions are called 'impredicative' definitions). The intuitionist regards a definition as 'constructing' the entity being defined; but he maintains that a set cannot be regarded as existing unless it has previ-

---

[1] For another quite different line of thought that has led some philosophers to reject the law of excluded middle, see Richard Taylor, *Metaphysics*, pp. 66-67, Prentice-Hall Foundations of Philosophy Series.

ously been 'constructed' by our deciding what its members are. So he thinks that an impredicative definition cannot succeed in constructing anything, since it presupposes the existence of that which it supposedly is generating. Another important victim of the intuitionist's scruples would be the 'axiom of choice,' which was first stated by the German mathematician Zermelo and shown by him to be an essential assumption in many arguments that have to do with infinite sets. According to the axiom of choice, for any set whose members are sets that are non-empty and mutually exclusive, there exists at least one set having exactly one element in common with each of the sets belonging to the original set. The intuitionist's objection to the axiom of choice is that this set which is declared to exist cannot be 'constructed'; to 'construct' the set we would have to state a rule enabling us, for any given object, to determine, through some finite process of counting or calculating, whether that object belongs to the set. No such rule is available for the kind of set that the axiom of choice declares to exist.

Thus intuitionism, the most influential form of conceptualistic philosophy of number, works considerable havoc upon classical mathematics by rejecting some of its methods of reasoning and some of its axioms. Is the philosophy behind intuitionism attractive enough to make this price seem worth while? Surely not. The whole doctrine that numbers and sets are brought into being by pure intuition of the process of counting is an exceedingly woolly and objectionable doctrine, if taken at all literally. What is this 'pure intuition' supposed to be? What proof is there that the mind can count only at finite speed in 'pure intuition'? Mightn't the mind count infinitely fast in 'pure intuition' and thus 'construct' transfinite numbers? The strangeness of the doctrine is thrown sharply into relief when we realize that it is a consequence of Kant's theory, and presumably of Brouwer's, that the laws of number hold true only of things as the mind intuits (senses) them, not of things as they are in themselves. The view that number is inapplicable to things as they really are in themselves means that things in reality are neither one nor many. This is too close to self-contradiction to be plausible.

The intuitionist's philosophical view about the creation of mathematical entities can of course be separated from his principles of mathematical practice (his rejection of non-constructive arguments, impredicative definitions, and so on). But without the philosophical view, the principles of mathematical practice seem arbitrary and unjustified. Why should one insist upon rejection of certain sorts of mathematical procedures hitherto generally accepted, unless this is done on the basis of some such philosophical doctrine as this?

Nominalism and conceptualism both are niggardly and grudging in their attitude towards questions of mathematical existence. The attitude of realism, in contrast, is one of generous amplitude, welcoming a profusion of abstract entities. Unlike the nominalist, the realist has no discriminatory prejudice against abstract entities as such. Unlike the conceptualist, he does not feel that the realm of abstract entities is in any way limited by the mind's poor power to create, for abstract entities exist in and of themselves, not as 'constructed' by the mind. The realist believes that there literally do exist whatever entities the axioms and theorems of number theory seem to speak of. This view about the interpretation of number theory is the most straightforward possible: whenever terms in number theory seem to refer to abstract entities they should be interpreted as doing so, and under such an interpretation the axioms and theorems are true statements.

From the realist's point of view, the task of the mathematician may be compared to a voyage of discovery. The mathematician cannot create or invent the objects of which he speaks, but they are there waiting for him to discover and describe them. As Bertrand Russell put it in one of his early writings:

> All knowledge must be recognition, on pain of being mere delusion; Arithmetic must be discovered in just the same sense in which Columbus discovered the West Indies, and we no more create numbers than he created the Indians . . . Whatever can be thought of has being, and its being is a precondition, not a result, of its being thought of.[2]

From the realist's point of view, there does not seem to be any justification for rejecting non-constructive proofs and impredicative definitions in mathematical reasoning, or for thinking that a statement may be neither true nor false (contrary to the law of excluded middle). If numbers and other mathematical entities are real independently of us, then the conceptualist's scruples all are urged in vain. There is nothing objectionable about non-constructive reasoning: Cantor's proof speaks of a real number whose infinitely long decimal representation we cannot run through, but that is all right, since the reality of the number does not depend on our being able to run through its decimal representation. Cantor has characterized a genuine number, even though we cannot determine specifically what real number it is. Similarly with impredicative definitions: if we view sets as existing in their own right independently of our thinking, then we can feel free in defining an entity to refer to a class that contains it. Moreover, the law of excluded

[2] Bertrand Russell, "Is Position in Space and Time Absolute or Relative?" *Mind*, X (1901), 312.

middle need not and must not be denied, for since the natural numbers exist, Fermat's last theorem, for instance, is either true for them or false for them; it must be one or the other, regardless of whether we can ever prove which.

What sort of knowledge will our knowledge of numbers be, according to realism? Here the situation becomes more difficult. The German mathematician Frege, who was the clearest and most forceful proponent of this realistic viewpoint, maintained that our knowledge of number is essentially a matter of a priori rational insight. (Russell, on the whole, agreed.) For Frege, it is a priori knowledge that we attain through use of 'the eye of Reason,' seeing into the timeless structures of numerical reality. Thus, this knowledge is not analytic in the first of the two senses of the word "analytic" that we distinguished before: that is, for Frege, knowledge of numbers is not basically a matter of understanding the meanings of words. When he speaks of Reason being acquainted with mathematical objects, this definitely entails that there is basically more to this kind of mathematical knowledge than understanding of language; it entails that someone might understand the language for numbers as fully as you please, yet if his Reason were clouded so that he failed to apprehend numbers, he would not know the laws of number.

Is Frege's view of our knowledge of number then just a version of the old rationalistic claim that the eye of Reason can gaze into the core of reality? No, not quite. For Frege (joined by Russell a little later) made a very important innovation in the philosophy of number: he held that the laws of number are all analytic. He wrote:

> In arithmetic we are not concerned with objects which we come to know as something alien from without . . . but with objects given directly to our reason and, as its nearest kin, utterly transparent to it.[3]

To the reader accustomed to present-day uses and misuses of the word "analytic" in philosophy, the quotation may sound like a strange way of expressing the view that our knowledge of number is analytic. But Frege employs the word "analytic" only in the second of the two senses that we distinguished. In holding that the laws of number are analytic, Frege is holding nothing more and nothing less than that they are 'reducible' to the laws of logic (when logic is understood broadly). Thus, to say that the laws of number are analytic in this second sense is perfectly compatible with saying that our knowledge of them basically depends upon rational insight. However, it must be the same sort of rational insight as that which gives us knowledge of the laws

---

[3] Gottlob Frege, *The Foundations of Arithmetic*, trans. J. L. Austin (Oxford: Basil Blackwell & Mott, 1953), p. 115e.

of logic; and this Frege regards as the very clearest and most direct sort of rational insight.

The doctrine that all the laws of the mathematics of number are derivable from, or can be 'reduced to,' logic alone, has come to be known as 'the logistic thesis.' First stated by Frege, it was later independently formulated by Russell, and in their monumental work, *Principia Mathematica*, Whitehead and Russell undertook to establish the thesis in detail. According to the logistic thesis, the laws of arithmetic and the rest of the mathematics of number are related to those of logic in the same way as the theorems of geometry are related to its axioms. If it is to be shown that this is so, two main things are required: a clear formulation of what the laws of logic are, and a series of definitions of the key terms of number theory which will permit its laws to be deduced from those of logic. It would have been out of the question to derive any part of mathematics from the traditional Aristotelian logic; a much more powerful system of logic than that is required. Frege and Whitehead and Russell contributed in very important ways to working out the laws of this modern and more powerful logic. It is essential to notice that, for their purposes, the terms "set" and "ordered pair" and the laws governing sets and ordered pairs were counted as belonging to logic, rather than to mathematics. (Russell did at one point propose what he called a 'no class' theory, but it was a theory that did without classes—another name for sets—only by using instead the equally or more complicated notions of properties and relations.)

The definitions needed were definitions of all the basic nonlogical terms and symbols of number theory; that includes "zero," "immediate successor," "natural number," and "+" and "×." The procedure of Whitehead and Russell was to define the natural numbers as certain kinds of sets of sets. Zero is defined as the set of all empty sets; one as the set of all non-empty sets each of which is such that any things belonging to it are identical; two as the set of all sets each having a member distinct from some other member but each being such that any member is identical with one or the other of these; and so on. One such set of sets is said to be the immediate successor of another if and only if, when one member is removed from any set belonging to the former, then the diminished set belongs to the latter.

Now, the set of natural numbers is a set to which belongs zero and to which belongs every immediate successor of something that belongs. To say this, however, is not to characterize the natural numbers fully, for there are many such sets (e.g., the set of all Frenchmen and natural numbers). What we can say, however, is that all the natural numbers, and they alone, belong to every such set. Thus a natural number can be defined as anything belonging to every set to which zero belongs and to which belongs the immediate successor of anything that belongs. Definitions of what it can mean to add and multiply these natural numbers can also be supplied, and then, with a developed logic which gives laws for sets and ordered pairs (or their equivalents) Peano's axioms and the rest of the laws of number theory can be deduced.

Frege maintained only that the laws of number could be reduced to logic in this manner. Whitehead and Russell had a more ambitious thesis, for they held that all mathematics can be reduced to logic. Geometry would have to be handled through analytic geometry, the points of space being identified with triads of real numbers. Abstract forms of algebra (which do not employ number) could be regarded as deriving from the logic of relations which Whitehead and Russell developed.

It is no accident that the logistic thesis was developed by advocates of realism as a philosophy of number, for these two views go naturally together. To be sure, someone who did not embrace realism might conceivably accept the logistic thesis, or vice versa. It was realism, however, which supplied the motivating intellectual drive behind the work of Frege and Russell, and had they been devotees of nominalism, of the Kantian conceptualism, or of some nonliteralistic philosophy of number, it is less likely that they would have developed the logistic thesis. As it was, they visualized themselves as explorers of a hitherto unknown level of abstract reality, explorers who were able to discover that the vast region of mathematical reality is really only a peninsula of the larger continent of logical reality. It was a bracing and exhilarating way of picturing one's own activity. But like many bright and fresh morning visions, it had begun to fade even before it came clearly into focus.

TRANSITION

TO A NONLITERALISTIC VIEW

OF NUMBER

5

In the later sections of the preceding chapter we were considering the question whether numbers literally exist, and we looked at three sorts of philosophical answer to that question. When these three philosophical answers were considered just in and of themselves, it seems fair to say that the third viewpoint, realism, is less unattractive and is more plausible than are the others. Only the third viewpoint regards all of classical mathematics as literally true. And when its realism is combined with the logistic thesis, it permits us to regard mathematical knowledge as no more mysterious than is our knowledge of logic (though no less so, either, of course). This third viewpoint won a considerable measure of acceptance among many philosophers. As we look back upon it, however, we find that distance lends disenchantment. There are some important technical developments in mathematical logic which tend to make the realistic viewpoint seem distinctly less attractive than it did at first.

The paradoxes   In ordinary language the term "paradox" can be used to refer to situations that have the appearance of being impossible or even self-contradictory yet which nevertheless hold true. It is in this sense that one might call it a paradox that according to Cantor's theory there are the same number of odd numbers as of natural numbers. In another sense, we call it a paradox when an argument which appears to be perfectly sound reasoning reaches an absurdly false conclusion. Zeno's famous paradoxes were arguments which looked sound and yet which reached the absurdly false conclusion that nothing in the world ever moves. There is a third sense, however, in which we may speak of paradoxes: this is when we have a situation in which, by reasoning that seems perfectly sound, we can show both that something must be true and that it must be false (paradoxes of this third sort are sometimes called antinomies). Examples of situations like this were collected by medieval logicians under the title of "sophismata"; but from even earlier times we have the example of the paradox of Epimenides. (This paradox must have been known in Roman times, for St. Paul in his *Epistle to Titus* refers to the Cretan who said all Cretans lie—though Paul evidently missed the point of the paradox.) To formulate the paradox of Epimenides we must assume (i) that Epimenides was a Cretan; (ii) that he stated that Cretans always lie; (iii) that all other statements by Cretans were lies. Each of these assumptions considered separately looks as though it could perfectly well be true, and it seems that all three ought to be capable of being true together. But if they were all true, then what of Epimenides' statement: would it be true or would it be false? To suppose that he spoke truly would entail that what he said was false, while to suppose that he spoke falsely would entail that what he said was true. Hence the situation is paradoxical, for it seems that Epimenides' statement would have to be both true and false. Paradoxes of this sort were puzzling, but down through the ages logicians did not attach much significance to them. They felt that paradoxes like this surely involve some trifling sort of verbal confusion, difficult to unravel but not essentially important. That comfortable illusion has been shattered in recent times.

Around the beginning of the present century, paradoxes of this third sort came to life with a vengeance, in a place where they could not be dismissed as unimportant. It was discovered that several such paradoxes arise out of the basic assumptions of set theory, when that theory is understood in a straightforward or 'naive' way. Cantor, perhaps as early as 1895, became aware of one important paradox in his theory of transfinite numbers. Later called 'Cantor's paradox,' this has to do with the entire set of cardinal numbers, finite and infinite: has it a cardinal number or not? It had been an assumption of Cantor's theory that every set has a cardinal number, so that would make the answer affirmative. Yet the answer cannot be affirmative, for the number of all the cardinals must be larger than any cardinal number. Here is an outright contradiction that emerges from pursuing Cantor's line of thought straightforwardly.

If Cantor's theory of transfinite numbers gives rise to a contradiction, should we just abandon the theory that there are transfinite numbers? That such a move would not suffice is shown by a still more disturbing paradox discovered by Russell in 1901. Russell's line of thought was as follows. In discussing sets it had always been assumed that for every statable condition there must exist a set containing all and only those things that satisfy that condition. That is, it was assumed that the schematic sentence:

1]   There exists a set such that whatever x may be, x is a member of it if and only if ...x...

comes out true no matter how we fill in the blank with a condition that x is to satisfy. For example, if we choose the condition "a dog barks at x at high noon," then (1) becomes "There exists a set such that whatever x may be, x is a member of it if and only if a dog barks at x at high noon." Or, if the condition is that of being a horse, then (1) becomes the statement "There exists a set such that whatever x may be, x is a member of it if and only if x is a horse." If the condition is that of not being a horse, then there exists the set to which belong all non-horses and nothing else. If the condition is that of being a unicorn, then there exists the set such that anything belongs to it if and only if it is a unicorn (this set will be the empty set). It was taken for granted that all these sets do exist. Now, some sets are not members of themselves: the set of horses is not a horse and therefore is not a member of itself; nor is the set of unicorns a member of itself, for it is not a unicorn. However, it would seem that some other sets are members of themselves; for example, the set of non-horses would seem to belong to itself, since it satisfies the condition of not being a horse; and the set of things mentioned in this book is something mentioned in this book, and therefore would seem to be a member of itself. In the light of this, let us consider filling the gap in (1) with the condition "x is a set that is not a member of itself." It seemed self-evident that (1) would come out true no matter how the gap is filled, so long as it is filled so as to make sense; therefore we ought to be able to fill in this condition and obtain:

2]   There exists a set such that whatever x may be, x is a member of it if and only if x is a set that is not a member of itself.

This statement (2) asserts the existence of a set of all sets that are not members of themselves. If we take it as established that there exists such a set, then we can give it a name—let us call it "k"—and we can go on to ask questions concerning it. In particular, let us ask: is this set k a member of itself? Here it seems self-evident that we may assert:

3]   Either k is a member of k or k is not a member of k.

Suppose k were a member of itself; then it would fail to fulfill the condition that anything must fulfill in order to belong to k; and therefore k is not a member of itself. On the other hand, suppose that k were not a member of itself; it would thereby fulfill the condition that is sufficient to make it a member of itself; and so it must be a member of itself. Thus we have proved that there is a set k which both is and is not a member of itself; and this is an outright contradiction.

Russell's contradiction is of the greatest importance because it brings to light a fundamental inconsistency at the heart of set theory, as set theory had been understood. Mathematicians such as Cantor and Frege had taken for granted that (1) and (3) were self-evidently true laws about sets; Russell's paradox shows that their unguarded attitude leads to a disastrous consequence. Should we then abandon set theory, denying that there are any such entities as sets? That would be a way out of the paradox, but it would be a very violent means of escape. For set theory is essential to the arithmetization of analysis, to the logistic thesis, and is much used in many parts of mathematics. To reject sets entirely would be to deal a crippling blow to mathematics. Is there perhaps some reasonable and less violent way of avoiding such paradoxes as these, through restricting the basic assumptions of set theory so as to restore consistency yet still to allow the derivation of useful theorems concerning sets?

The theory of types Russell himself took a comparatively sanguine view of the significance of the paradoxes. He believed that set theory could be restored to consistency in a form strong enough to be adequate for mathematics, and he believed that this could be done in an inherently credible way, consonant with common sense. He held this sanguine view because he believed that the paradoxes all had a common root in their violation of a definitely valid rule which he called 'the vicious circle principle.' He formulated this principle in the slogan, "If, provided a certain collection had a total, it would have members only definable in terms of that total, then the said collection has no total." The reasoning involved in the paradox of Epimenides violates this rule because in trying to express what Epimenides said one refers to the totality, or set, of all statements made by Cretans, to which would belong the very statement one is trying to express. Cantor's paradox violates the principle because in defining the number of the cardinal numbers one refers to the totality, or set, of all cardinals, to which this number being defined would belong. Russell's paradox violates the principle because in defining the set of all sets not members of themselves it refers to the totality of all such sets, to which would belong the very set being defined.

In their book *Principia Mathematica* Whitehead and Russell of course were not just concerned to avoid these specific paradoxes, and the others known to them. They sought to restrict their axioms relating to sets in such a fashion that all kindred paradoxes would be avoided. For this purpose they introduced what they called "the theory of types," whose aim was to give a rigorous technical formulation to the vicious circle principle. The original theory of types was quite complex, but its basic idea was that all the entities referred to in set theory, including sets, set of sets, sets of sets of sets, and so on, are to be thought of as arranged in a hierarchy of levels, or types, each entity belonging to just one definite type. To the lowest type belong individuals—that is, all and only those entities that are not sets. To the next higher type belong sets whose members are entities of the lowest type; to the third type belong sets whose members are entities of the second type; and in general, to the type $n + 1$ belong sets of entities of the nth type. Only entities that fit into the types of this hierarchy are to be recognized by set theory; we are not to be allowed to speak of any set having members of types other than the type next lower than its own. However, the theory of types does not deny the existence of such sets; its approach is more radical than that. What it denies is the very meaningfulness of sentences which try to speak about the membership of entities in sets other than those of the next higher type. According to the theory of types, sentences which attempt to do so are neither true nor false, but are logically ill-formed: they are nonsensical sentences. Unlike the intuitionists, Whitehead and Russell did not reject the law of excluded middle. They did not believe that there are any meaningful statements which are neither true nor false; instead they held that some seemingly meaningful sentences really are nonsense, and do not express statements at all.

Thus the theory of types injected the very important notion of nonsense into logic, and thereby into philosophy: the notion that even a sentence which looks as though it made sense can nevertheless covertly be nonsensical. By doing so, the theory of types enabled Whitehead and Russell in *Principia Mathematica* to avoid the paradoxes, and to do so without rejecting as false the attractive principle (1) discussed in the preceding section. According to the theory of Whitehead and Russell, for any statable condition there does exist a set whose members are all and only the things satisfying that condition. However, the theory of types imposes a limitation upon what kind of conditions count as statable. In particular, the condition used in obtaining (2) of the previous section is rejected as nonsensical, and therefore (2) is neither true nor false, and Russell's paradox is thus prevented from arising.

Russell's view seems to have been that the theory of types provided the way of avoiding all the paradoxes, and moreover that it was the inherently reasonable way of doing so. Let us consider these two points in turn.

More recent writers have distinguished, as Russell did not, between what are called 'semantical' paradoxes and the paradoxes of set theory. The paradox of Epimenides is called a semantical paradox because it essentially involves the notion of truth (lies are untrue); and truth is called a semantical relation because it is a relation between language and nonlinguistic reality. More recent writers have come to feel that the theory of types is not the way to handle the semantical paradoxes, and that they need separate treatment. Tarski's so-called semantical theory of truth provides a now quite generally accepted way of avoiding the semantical paradoxes. According to Tarski's theory, the term "true" must always be understood as relative to a specified language; we should not just say of a sentence that it is true, rather we should say that it is true-in-English, or true-in-*Principia Mathematica*, etc. The way to avoid semantical paradoxes is to require that the notion of being true in language L must not be expressible in language L itself. If we want to talk about truth in L, then we must speak in another language, say L', which is called a meta-language. If we abide by this restriction then assumption (ii) upon which the Epimenides paradox depended becomes the harmless assumption that Epimenides said in some meta-language L' that all statements made by Cretans in their Cretan language L fail to be true-in-L. The paradox cannot now arise. The theory of types does not deal clearly with these semantical paradoxes, which need to be handled instead by this semantical theory of truth.

The theory of types does of course serve to prevent paradoxes such as Cantor's and Russell's paradoxes from arising in set theory. Is it the reasonable way of doing so? We notice that the 'vicious circle principle' as Russell informally expounds it is a rejection of just those impredicative definitions (definitions which, in defining a thing, refer to some totality to which the thing being defined belongs) which intuitionists deplore. Yet Russell's avowed philosophy was that of realism, and realism offers no philosophical rationale for rejecting impredicative definitions. If a set has independent reality, then why may not members of the set be defined by reference to the set itself? The intuitionist's picture of mathematical entities as being progressively generated by the mind gave a rationale (though only a woolly one) to the claim that impredicative definition is a viciously circular procedure; the realist's philosophy offers no rationale at all, not even a woolly one. Thus Russell surely was exaggerating when he claimed that the theory of types was inherently reasonable. On the contrary, its character is that of an arbitrary makeshift device for stopping the paradoxes.

The makeshift character of Russell's viewpoint is confirmed by some of its unattractive consequences. One of these unattractive consequences has to do with the infinity of the natural numbers. The natural numbers were defined as certain sets of sets. Now, according to the theory of types, the members of the sets that are members of the natural numbers must all be entities of the same type, presumably of the lowest type. If there existed only a finite number of entities of that lowest type, then there would be some maximum finite size to the sets of such entities (a set containing them all would have this maximum size). But in that case there would be a largest natural number (it would be the set of maximum-sized sets of entities of the lowest type). However, it is a law of number theory that there is no largest natural number. In order to be able to deduce this law as a theorem of *Principia Mathematica,* Whitehead and Russell found it necessary to introduce what they called the axiom of infinity. This is an axiom asserting the existence of infinitely many entities of the lowest type. The unattractive thing about this axiom is that it does not jibe with the philosophy of realism, according to which the mathematics of number is just supposed to express what we can know a priori about certain abstract entities. These entities of the lowest type presumably are not abstract entities but are physical objects or other observable particular things. How can we know that there exist infinitely many such entities? It seems impossible to know this by inductive reasoning based on the evidence of the senses. Can we know it a priori by rational insight? Frege and Russell had spoken as if the 'eye of Reason' could penetrate in logic into the timeless abstract structures of reality, and into them alone. The view that rational insight could enable us to know of the existence of particular observable objects was supposed to have been long since discredited. Thus the axiom of infinity has an unsatisfactory status.

Moreover, the theory of types has technical consequences that are unattractive in further ways. In the customary theory of sets, there is one universal set to which everything belongs, one empty set to which nothing belongs, and to each set there corresponds a complementary set containing all non-members of the given set. These laws can no longer hold if the theory of types is adopted, for it allows a set to have members only of a uniform type. The result is that there will be an infinite series of 'universal' sets, one for each type, and a similar series of empty sets, one for each type. The 'complement' of a given set, instead of containing all non-members of the given set, can contain only those non-members that are of the next lower type. Still more distressing is the result that there occurs an infinite reduplication of the natural numbers. According to the logistic thesis, the number one is a set of single-membered sets; and according to the theory of types, these single-membered sets must all be of the same type, presumably of the type that is one level above the lowest type. This number one is the number we want in connection with counting objects of the lowest type. But if we wish to count things of some higher type, we must define another distinct number one, which will be a set of single-membered sets of higher type. We get a new number one for each additional level in the type hierarchy, and the same for each of the other natural numbers. The natural numbers thus cease to be unique, and a separate array of laws must pertain to the numbers of each type. (In order to minimize type difficulties, Russell introduced what he called "the axiom of reducibility," which in effect allows his set theory to employ impredicative definitions and thus provides freedom to develop classical mathematics: but this is a non-constructive axiom, and some of his critics felt that it is not self-evidently true.)

The theory of types certainly was an immensely important contribution to mathematical logic, for it made possible the consistent working out of *Principia Mathematica*. By distinguishing so sharply among types, however, it produced this unattractive reduplication of entities, and it made difficult or impossible the stating and proving of some traditional theorems. The original claim that the theory of types was inherently credible because of its consonance with common sense was too strong a claim.

Other ways around the paradoxes The theory of types would have had a greater claim to be regarded as inherently credible if it had been the only known way of avoiding the paradoxes. This was not so, however. During the earlier years of the present century three other quite separate lines of thought were advanced as ways of organizing set theory so as to avoid these inconsistencies.

The intuitionists did not need, nor would they have accepted, Whitehead's and Russell's theory of types; for their own philosophy of mathematics gave them other ways of avoiding the paradoxes. Indeed, the intuitionists were inclined to welcome the paradoxes, for the paradoxes seemed to them gratifyingly to demonstrate the weakness of nonintuitionistic mathematics. Believing as they did that mathematical entities are 'constructed' by the mind, they would of course have agreed with Russell that it is viciously circular to suppose that one can define a set that will be the set of all sets not members of themselves. But the flaw in this definition, they would have felt, is not that it violates the theory of types; rather, the flaw in the definition is the impossibility through constructive intuition, of bringing into being the set of all sets not members of themselves. Moreover, the intuitionists would have thought the theory of types too restrictive in some ways (some of the sets that it forbids us to speak of, such as the set of *all* empty sets, do seem to be constructible), but not nearly restrictive enough in other ways (for the theory of types permits such nonconstructive assertions as the axiom of reducibility and the axiom of choice).

Furthermore, intuitionism has another line of defense against the paradoxes. Believing that all mathematical truth and falsity must be 'constructible,' the intuitionist rejects the traditional law of the excluded middle; he feels that there may well be meaningful statements which are neither true nor false. Therefore, in dealing with a paradoxical argument, even if he cannot find in it some definition that contains a flaw, the intuitionist still will not feel obliged to accept the reasoning if it employs the law of excluded middle. He can simply regard the seemingly contradictory conclusions as neither true nor false, and thus not necessarily in conflict with each other. The intuitionist's way of avoiding the paradoxes, resting as it does upon his cloudy philosophy of mental 'construction,' perhaps is not more attractive than is the theory of types of Whitehead and Russell: but the point is that it is not much less attractive, either.

Another quite different approach to set theory was that first proposed by Zermelo shortly before the appearance of *Principia Mathematica*, and later further developed by Fränkel. Unlike Whitehead and Russell, Zermelo and Fränkel did not impose limitations upon what sentences are to be regarded as making sense, and unlike the intuitionists they did not abandon the traditional laws of logic. What they did was to reject the principle that for every statable condition there exists a set having as members the things fulfilling that condition. Rejection of this principle enabled them to avoid Cantor's and Russell's paradoxes—for those paradoxes cannot arise unless it is supposed that there does exist a set of all cardinal numbers and that there does exist a set of all sets not belonging to themselves. Removing from set theory this principle of unrestricted set existence does stop the paradoxes from arising; but of course it would totally cripple set theory if one simply rejected that principle and did not replace it by anything else. Zermelo's idea was to replace it by a variety of axioms that assert the existence of sets of certain well-behaved kinds, but from which the existence of ill-behaved sets cannot be inferred. Among Zermelo's axioms are these: that given any two objects, there exists a set having just these as its members; that there exists the set of all members of members of a given set; that the set of all subsets of a given set exists; and, especially important, that given any set there exists the set of all members of it that satisfy any statable condition. In Zermelo's set theory there does exist a unique empty set, but no universal set can be proved to exist. Nor can it be proved that the complement of any set (i.e., the set containing all non-members of the given set) exists. With a set theory such as Zermelo's, the problem, of course, is to introduce strong enough axioms so that the existence can be proved of enough sets to make possible the deduction of as many as possible of the desired theorems concerning sets, while yet keeping the axioms sufficiently restricted so that the paradoxes cannot arise. A compromise has to be struck, sacrificing some desired richness in order to preserve consistency.

A fourth, still different method of organizing set theory originated with von Neumann. His approach differed from that of Zermelo, for instead of restricting the existence of sets, von Neumann introduced the novel idea that not all entities are capable of membership in sets. He divided entities into two kinds: elements and non-elements. Only the former can belong to sets. He then introduced axioms to provide for the elementhood of certain well-behaved entities (roughly the same well-behaved sets whose existence Zermelo's axioms assert, are asserted to be elements by von Neumann's axioms).

We thus have four different approaches to the problem posed by the paradoxes of set theory. The intuitionists can avoid the paradoxes by abandoning nonconstructive axioms and definitions and the logical law of the excluded middle as well. Whitehead and Russell avoid them by narrowing the range of sentences in set theory that are to count as making sense. Zermelo avoids them by limiting his assumptions concerning the existence of sets. Von Neumann avoids them by limiting his assumptions concerning elementhood. Each of these approaches is able to preserve substantial parts of traditional set theory, yet none preserves all the laws of sets that might seem desirable. There is an arbitrary, makeshift air about each of these four approaches; yet nothing better is in sight. This situation is very much at odds with what the philosophy of realism would have led us to expect. If sets are abstract entities which really exist independently of the mind, awaiting discovery by it, then one would expect to be able to produce some single, clearly best theory of sets. It no longer seems plausible to suppose that this can be done.

Formalized deductive systems   Discovery of the paradoxes in set theory showed that concealed contradictions could be contained even in basic principles which had seemed simple and self-evidently correct. This focused attention anew upon the problem of consistency. Could there be any way of establishing that the revised deductive systems for set theory and number theory, such as *Principia Mathematica* with its theory of types, were free from inconsistency and would not eventually give rise to contradictions also? The two methods for establishing consistency which we previously considered are of little value here. To establish the consistency of, say, *Principia Mathematica*, directly by finding an interpretation under which its axioms all come out indubitably true is not practicable. No interpretation could make the axioms of *Principia Mathematica* come out true unless it referred to infinite arrays of things; and any interpretation that does this is going to be rather questionable as regards its truth. Nor could relative proofs of consistency carry us very far; to show that, say, von Neumann's set theory is consistent if Zermelo's is, does not give us any firm basis for feeling confident of the consistency of either one.

Faced with this situation, Hilbert proposed a new method for investigating questions such as consistency, a method which has come to be known as meta-mathematics. It involves adopting a view of deductive systems even more coldly abstract than the abstract viewpoint which we previously considered (there all words or symbols of logic were regarded as retaining their normal meanings—only nonlogical words were viewed as uninterpreted). From this new viewpoint we pay no attention to the meanings of *any* of the symbols or terms occurring in the system. We regard the system in a completely *formalized* way: that is, we pay attention only to the way strings of marks go together to make up theorems in the system—what any of the marks mean, or whether they say anything that is true, we neglect entirely.

In describing a system in this formalized way we first must specify the 'formation rules' of the system; that is, the rules determining what combinations of marks are permissible and count as well-formed formulas of the system. Some but not all of these well-formed formulas ought to count as theorems of the system. In order to characterize what it is to be a theorem we first must specify which of these well-formed formulas are to count as axioms; and then we must specify what 'transformation rules' the system has; that is, what the rules are for obtaining new formulas from ones that we already have. A proof can then be characterized as any sequence of well-formed formulas such that each formula in the sequence is either an axiom or is obtained by some transformation rule from earlier well-formed formulas in the sequence. Finally, a theorem can be characterized as any well-formed formula that is the last formula in some proof sequence.

Viewed in this way, the formalized system is like a game played with marks. To play the game, we start with certain initial combinations of marks (the axioms) and we are allowed to use certain transformations in order to obtain further combinations of marks (the theorems). We can study this game and discover facts about what can and what cannot be accomplished in it, without ever needing to consider the meanings of any marks occurring in the game itself. However, the statements that we make about the game are not themselves moves within the game. Here we must distinguish between the symbols and formulas of the system under study and the symbols we use and the statements we make in describing that system. The latter belong not to the system but to our meta-language, the language in which we conduct our meta-mathematical study. The rigorous pursuit of meta-mathematics will consist in proving certain meta-theorems, which are stated in the meta-language. These meta-theorems are statements which talk about the marks of the system under study and which describe the moves that can ᴖr cannot be made in that system according to its rules.

Now, the point of this procedure of formalizing a system is to enable us to investigate its logical properties, such as consistency. For an interpreted system, one way of posing the question of consistency is to ask whether there is any statement such that both it and its denial are theorems of the system. With regard to a formalized system, the analogue of that question is the question whether there is any well-formed formula such that it is provable according to the rules of the game both when it has and when it does not have the mark "—" prefixed to it (assuming that "—" is the mark which normally would be understood as expressing denial, when prefixed to a sentence). If the answer is yes the formalized system is inconsistent. (This way of speaking of consistency would have to be modified, of course, for formalized systems not containing any symbol that is normally understood as expressing denial). We may hope that investigating consistency in this way will enable us to establish consistency in cases where it would not otherwise be possible to do so.

Of course, if meta-mathematical reasoning is to succeed in establishing consistency, it must itself employ principles that are simple enough so as to be comparatively free of suspicion. Hilbert's procedure was to restrict meta-mathematical reasoning wholly to what are called constructive methods. Thus, a meta-theorem to the effect that something is true of every well-formed formula must be understood as providing a method by which for any given well-formed formula a finite series of steps will demonstrate specifically that this thing holds true of it. A meta-theorem to the effect that something holds true of at least one well-formed formula must be understood as providing a method by which a finite series of steps will suffice to identify such a well-formed formula and to demonstrate specifically that this thing holds true of it. Hilbert restricted meta-mathematical reasoning to methods that are constructive in this sense not because he accepted the philosophy of intuitionism, but because those constructive methods, being more limited in scope, are markedly less doubtful as regards their consistency than is the nonconstructive reasoning of systems such as *Principia Mathematica.* Hilbert felt that all mathematicians, including intuitionists, could thus agree about the validity of meta-mathematical reasoning. Intuitionists might regard the formalized systems under study as incapable of being interpreted so as to come out true; yet nevertheless they should accept the meta-theorems that were proved about these systems.

Incompletability   In addition to the question of consistency, another important question to ask about deductive systems is the question of their completeness. The idea of completeness is the idea that nothing which ought to be a theorem of the system fails to be provable as a theorem. An interpreted system of geometry, for example, would be said to be complete (deductively complete) provided that every true statement expressible in its primitive terms is a theorem. In talking about the completeness of an uninterpreted system we would not want to discuss truth, so we reformulate the idea of completeness thus: to say that an uninterpreted system is complete is to say that there is no sentence expressible in the primitive terms of the system such that neither it nor its denial is provable as a theorem of the system. Analogously, a formalized system is said to be complete provided that each well-formed formula is a theorem either when it is written without or when it is written with the mark "—" prefixed (again assuming that this mark is one that occurs in the system and one that would normally be interpreted as expressing denial). Completeness is a desirable property for a system to have, of course. If an interpreted system is incomplete, this means that there are truths about its subject matter which cannot be deduced from its axioms; its axioms fail to capture all the information that we would have liked them to contain.

Hilbert's meta-mathematical method is appropriate for investigating completeness as well as consistency. Hilbert, and other mathematicians and logicians of the earlier part of this century, confidently hoped that it would eventually prove possible to develop each branch of mathematics in the form of an axiomatic system that could be shown to be both consistent and complete; or, better still, to develop one unified system for the whole of mathematics, which could be shown to be both consistent and complete. This attractive and plausible expectation was decisively destroyed by the work of Gödel in 1931. By an ingenious chain of meta-mathematical reasoning, Gödel was able to demonstrate that for systems of the most important kind, consistency is incompatible with completeness. Such systems, if consistent, must necessarily be incomplete.

The kind of systems which Gödel studied were those such as *Principia Mathematica*, whose primitive terms and axioms are rich enough to allow one to speak of the natural numbers and to deduce the laws governing such operations as addition and multiplication of them. The formulas of such a system, when interpreted in the intended way, speak of natural numbers; nevertheless, by means of a technique now called Gödel numbering, he was able to show how some formulas of the system must necessarily *reflect* meta-mathematical assertions about the system itself. That is, he was able to find a way of correlating certain formulas of the system with meta-mathematical statements about the system so that each such formula under its normal interpretation expresses a true statement about natural numbers just in case the meta-mathematical assertion with which it is correlated is true also.

In developing these correlations, Gödel started with the primitive signs of the system; for each primitive sign of the system a particular natural number is arbitrarily chosen and is defined as being its Gödel number. A definition is then offered of what numerical properties a number shall have in order to be called the Gödel number of a formula; and this is done in such a way that the Gödel number of any formula is a numerical function of the Gödel numbers of the primitive signs that occur in it and of their order of occurrence, so that given any Gödel number one can calculate what formula it belongs to. What it is for a number to be the Gödel number of a sequence of formulas can then be defined. Ultimately it is possible to define what numerical properties a number must have in order to be called the Gödel number of a proof; that is, the Gödel number of a sequence of formulas, each of which either is an axiom or is obtained from earlier formulas in the sequence by means of a transformation rule of the system. Then it is possible to define the numerical properties that a number must have in order to be called the Gödel number of a theorem (that is, the last formula in a sequence that is a proof); and thence to define the numerical properties that a number must have if it is to be called the Gödel number of a well-formed formula that is not a theorem.

These definitions are carefully constructed so that the assertions about Gödel numbers will be true just in case the meta-mathematical assertions associated with them are true. Thus, the assertion that a certain number has the numerical properties that entitle it to be called the Gödel number of a non-theorem will be true just in case the rules of the system do not make it possible to construct a proof of the formula whose Gödel number this number is. The assertions about

Gödel numbers are in turn correlated with formulas of the system: each assertion is correlated with the formula which, when its signs are interpreted in the normal way, will express that assertion. Thus, certain formulas of the system are correlated with assertions about Gödel numbers, and those in turn are correlated with meta-mathematical assertions, giving us a correlation between these formulas of the system and meta-mathematical assertions.

Now let us consider a formula which is correlated with the assertion that a specific natural number has those numerical properties that make it the Gödel number of a well-formed formula which is not a theorem. Since it can be interpreted as making a statement about a particular number, this formula has to contain a numeral (a sign, or sequence of signs, which under its normal interpretation would be understood as naming a particular number). The formula itself has a Gödel number, and to that Gödel number there corresponds some numeral. Now suppose that the numeral in this formula is the very numeral which corresponds to the Gödel number of the formula itself. Gödel showed how to write out a formula like this. Because of the way the formulas of the system reflect meta-mathematics, this special Gödelian formula (when normally interpreted) expresses a true statement about natural numbers just in case the meta-mathematical assertion with which it is correlated is true. That assertion is the assertion that this very formula is not a theorem. Thus we have a formula which is not a theorem if it expresses a truth about the natural numbers, and is a theorem if it expresses a falsehood about the natural numbers.

By further reasoning it is possible to demonstrate that the existence of this formula means that the system must be outright inconsistent if it is complete. It can be consistent only at the price of being incomplete, and can be complete only at the price of being inconsistent. In this sense, the system is said to be incompletable. Gödel's reasoning showed that this conclusion applies to any system rich enough to express the theory of the natural numbers; for in any such system some Gödelian formula can be constructed.

One way of formulating this conclusion is to say that any consistent axiomatization of the theory of the natural numbers must always fail to capture as theorems all the truths about the natural numbers. Some axiomatizations can capture more of the truths about natural numbers than others do, and for each truth there is some axiomatization in which it is captured; but no single consistent axiomatization can get them all. This result strikes a decisive blow against the idea that mathematical truth can be identified with deducibility from axioms.

A further conclusion which Gödel established as a consequence of this is that any meta-mathematical demonstration of the consistency of systems of this kind must employ meta-mathematical principles more complex than the principles embodied within the system under study. The consistency of a system such as *Principia Mathematica* cannot be demonstrated except in a meta-language that uses reasoning logically richer and more complex than that of *Principia Mathematica* itself. This result dashed Hilbert's hope of using generally accepted meta-mathematical methods to establish the consistency of mathematical systems; for it means that there are many systems such that if any meta-mathematical arguments can be given in favor of their consistency, these can only be arguments employing nonconstructive methods not acceptable to all mathematicians. Moreover, these methods must often be more complex and therefore more suspect as regards their consistency, than is the system under study.

Formalism   In the preceding chapter we considered literalistic views of the mathematics of number, views which hold that this mathematics possesses its intellectual value because its laws can be interpreted as important truths. Among these views, nominalism seemed incapable of providing any true interpretation, and conceptualism seemed to rest upon a cloudy and unsubstantiated doctrine regarding the mind's supposed creative powers. Realism seemed the least unpromising literalistic view. Yet realism does not stand up well in the light of subsequent developments. If the mathematics of number is the investigation of a field of independently real abstract entities such as sets and numbers, then there ought to be some one true body of laws about these entities. Yet in trying to meet the challenge of the paradoxes, mathematical logicians have developed four basically different kinds of theories, whose laws are by no means entirely in agreement. Each kind of theory is somewhat arbitrary and makeshift, and there seems to be no ground whatever for holding that one of these approaches is truer than the others. The presence of different, partly conflicting theories and the absence of any ground for calling one truer than the others make the realistic philosophy much less tenable than it seemed at first. We cannot feel that we are discovering truths about an independent reality, under these circumstances. Furthermore, Gödel's demonstration of the incompletability of number theory is another blow to the realistic philosophy. If it were an independent reality of sets and numbers that mathematics describes, then one would have expected that the truth about that reality, which would have to be consistent, should allow of being axiomatized completely. A reality the truth about which is necessarily incapable of being described in any complete manner seems a queer and suspect sort of reality—that is, not a reality at all.

Considerations such as these, reinforced also by nominalistic distaste for the doctrine of the reality of sets and numbers and for the doctrine of rational insight, have led many thinkers to the conclusion that the mathematics of number should not be viewed literalistically. Whatever may be the intellectual value of mathematics, their conclusion is that it does not reside in the truth of its descriptions of abstract reality.

We have seen that for the purposes of meta-mathematical study axiomatized mathematical systems can be regarded as formalized. That is, they can be regarded as games with marks, games in which certain strings of marks are derivable from others according to definite rules. Formalism, as a philosophy of mathematics, is the view that mathematical systems should basically be regarded as nothing but formalized systems. The advocate of formalism feels that by regarding mathematical systems just as formalized systems, he escapes a great many confusing and unnecessary questions. What do the laws of number mean? How do we know whether they are true? Do numbers exist? Such questions all evaporate and cannot even be asked, if the view of mathematical systems as nothing but formalized systems is adhered to. The formulas of such a formalized system do not mean anything, they are neither true nor false, they embody no knowledge and no claims about the existence of anything.

However, if we regard mathematics as a game played with meaningless marks, what then is the point of the game? Why is mathematics worth playing? Perhaps some formalists would reply that the game is worth playing and studying just for its own sake, like chess. But that cannot be the full answer, for it does not explain the enormous utility of mathematics for the sciences. How could a game played with meaningless marks be of such value to physics, engineering, and the like? The formalist can give a kind of answer to this without abandoning his view that basically mathematics is to be regarded as a game with meaningless marks. One line of thought for him is that the utility of the system results from the fact that its axioms and transformation rules can be used to derive significant empirical statements from one another. To illustrate the point crudely, the formula "$5 \times 70 \times 90 = 31{,}500$" is a theorem of arithmetic, which is derivable from the axioms according to the definitions and transformation rules. For the formalist, this theorem is just a string of marks, not a statement. The formula can be valuable, however, if we use it as a guide for manipulating empirical statements. The practical value of this formula is that, guided by it, from an empirical statement such as "The farm contains five fields each of seventy acres and needing ninety pounds of fertilizer per acre" we can derive the empirical statement "The farm needs 31,500 pounds of fertilizer." Each of these empirical statements is perfectly meaningful, and need not be thought of as mentioning abstract entities such as numbers. An empirical statement such as "The farm contains five fields" can be regarded as asserting merely that the procedure of counting the fields yields a certain result (pointing successively at each field as one speaks a word, the words "one," "two," "three," "four," "five" suffice); the statement need not be construed as talking about an unobservable abstract entity, the number five.

Now, a formalized system is valuable to science and engineering and agriculture, provided it leads us to make helpful derivations of empirical statements from one another. In order to be reliably helpful, it should never lead us to derive a false empirical statement from a true one. There could of course be a formalized system containing as a theorem the string of marks, "$5 \times 70 \times 90 = 15,300$"; but if we allowed that theorem to lead us to derive the empirical statement, "The farm needs 15,300 pounds of fertilizer," from the statement, "The farm contains five fields of seventy acres each needing ninety pounds of fertilizer per acre," then we would be led into agricultural difficulties. A system containing that theorem would not be so easy to apply fruitfully.

The normal arithmetic we use is highly useful because it never does lead us to derive a false empirical statement from a true one. How do we know this? The formalist, who is trying to get away from the (to him) repugnant idea of mathematical 'truth,' cannot reply that we know this because we know that arithmetic is true. If he gives any answer, it can only be that we know this by induction. Past experience shows that our standard arithmetic, when applied as we do apply it, does not lead us to derive false empirical statements from true ones.

Thus the view of the formalist will be that there is no such thing as meaning or truth in mathematical systems; those systems do not contain statements at all, but merely marks. One kind of system is never more 'correct' than another (assuming that both are properly formalized). When organized as formalized systems, the set theory of the intuitionists constitutes a different game with marks than does that of Zermelo or von Neumann, but they are all of them good games. Which shall we play? If one of them turns out in the long run to have applications in science that are more reliable and more fruitful than are the applications of the others, then that is a reason for preferring it. But we do not really have to choose among games; we can play them all, with catholic unconcern. Such would be the view of the formalist.

The point of view of formalism is valuable in helping us to escape from the notion that the laws of number must describe entities that are numbers. It is valuable in helping us to view arithmetic in terms of its actual application to empirical situations. Formalism is a very extreme view, however, when it insists that *all* the mathematics of number must be regarded as nothing but strings of marks which can say nothing true or false. Is not some less extreme position possible? Suppose we grant that the formulas of number mathematics should not be literalistically regarded as truths (i.e., we should not think of "zero" as the name of some entity that literally exists, etc.). May it not still be possible nonliteralistically to construe at least some of these formulas as expressing truths?

Suppose someone notices that the sentence, "The average U.S. undertaker earned $10,900 in 1962," cannot plausibly be given any literalistic interpretation under which it comes out true (neither through the senses nor through the eye of Reason are we acquainted with any such object as the average U.S. undertaker). Would that justify him in concluding that the sentence must be viewed as a string of marks incapable of expressing a true or false statement? Or suppose someone realizes that the sentence, "Spring has come," cannot plausibly be given any literalistic interpretation under which it comes out true (neither through the senses nor through rational insight are we acquainted with any such object as spring). Would that justify him in inferring that the sentence must be regarded as a string of marks incapable of expressing a true or false statement? In both cases the inference is unjustified and rests upon too narrow a notion of what it is to make a statement. Both these sentences are perfectly capable of expressing true statements, but in order to understand how they do so we must not interpret them literalistically—instead, we must construe them as involving *façons de parler*. To say that the average U.S. undertaker earned $10,900 in 1962 is not to say anything definite about any particular observable thing; but it is to say that if you add up the total income of U.S. undertakers in 1962 and divide by the number of undertakers, the quotient will be $10,900. To say that spring has come is not to say that any one particular object has arrived; but it is to say that many such things as the following have happened: the air has become balmy, the flowers have begun to sprout, the trees have burst into leaf, the swallows have returned to Capistrano, etc. When we construe them properly, we see that both these sentences can express perfectly good statements; it would be sheer misunderstanding to hold that they must be regarded merely as strings of marks.

Might it not be the same with formulas of number theory? Surely the formula "$5 \times 70 \times 90 = 31,500$" can perfectly well be construed as saying something true: it says that whenever you have five things, each having its own entirely distinct group of seventy things, for each of which an entirely distinct group of ninety things is required, then 31,500 things are required in all. We need not regard this statement as mentioning entities that are numbers; that would be too literalistic. Instead, we can regard it as talking about certain procedures of counting—procedures of successively uttering the words "one," "two," "three," etc., as one points. We can regard the statement as telling us about certain results of those procedures when they are carried out in the standard manner. It tells us that whenever we count five things, for each of which an entirely distinct group of seventy are counted, and for each of those, an entirely distinct group of ninety are counted, why then, the total number of things involved of this last kind will count up to 31,500, if counted directly. Thus, even when the sentence is not regarded as talking about numbers as abstract entities, it still can perfectly well be regarded as expressing a true statement. In this spirit, many of the formulas of the theory of natural numbers and of rational numbers can be construed as statements about what the results of various procedures of counting will be.

When understood in this way, what kind of knowledge do the theorems of this part of mathematics express? Do they express empirical knowledge, knowledge that we attain inductively by generalizing on the basis of our observations of how counting procedures have worked out in the past? John Stuart Mill held that they do, and that in this sense arithmetic is basically an inductive science, like physics and chemistry. The alternative is to hold that these theorems express a priori knowledge about what the results of counting *must* be, if the counting is correctly done. In reflecting on the contrast between these two views, let us suppose that someone goes to a farm, counts and recounts its fields and acres (we may imagine the acres to be separately marked off), comes back to us and says, "I counted five fields, and in each field seventy acres, and I counted 349 acres in all." Should we say (as Mill would have us say), "Well, possibly you are right. Possibly five times seventy don't always make 350. After all, arithmetic is inductive"? Or should we say, "Nonsense. If there really are five fields of seventy acres each, then there must necessarily be 350 acres. We cannot call your procedure correct counting unless you get this result. Perhaps your mistake occurred because some of the boundary lines were unclear or shifting"?

Here the situation is analogous to that in geometry: should we understand our terms in such a way that arithmetic is empirical, or should we understand them in such a way that arithmetic is a priori? Which way of speaking reflects the deeper tendency in our past usage of these number terms? Here again there is no perfectly decisive, clear-cut answer, for different tendencies are latent in our past usage. But if the laws of arithmetic were understood as inductive generalizations about the outcomes of counting procedures, then we ought to be able to describe what it would be like for experience to yield evidence that they are false (we are entitled to say that a generalization needs confirming by sense experience only if it is a generalization that sense experience also could conceivably refute). It does not seem possible, however, to give any very convincing or plausible description of what it would be like for the senses to indicate that, say, five times seventy is not equal to 350. This suggests that the view of laws of arithmetic as inductive generalizations about counting procedures is, on the whole, less plausible and less in accord with our use of number terminology than is the view that they are a priori truths about counting.

When they are understood as making a priori statements about the procedures of counting, are these laws of arithmetic analytic or are they synthetic? To say that they were analytic in our second sense (Frege's sole sense), would be to say that they could be reduced to laws of deductive logic, through appeal to definitions of the counting procedure. They do not seem to be analytic in this sense, though; for it does not appear possible to formulate explicit definitions of the procedures of counting that would suffice to permit us to reduce laws of arithmetic to laws of logic. The definitions of the notions of arithmetic in terms of sets and ordered pairs proposed by the logistic thesis are unhelpful and unilluminating when we are viewing arithmetical laws as statements about counting procedures. However, these laws of arithmetic when understood in this way are analytic in our first sense: they are laws such that nothing beyond understanding them is required in order to enable us to know that they are true. Someone who doubts or denies one of the basic laws of arithmetic thereby shows conclusively that he is not understanding it as we do. Understood in this spirit, these laws of arithmetic reflect our determination to regard certain uses of number words as linguistically proper uses and to regard other uses as linguistically improper.

Not all the mathematics of number can be construed as expressing statements about the results of correct counting, however. When we pass beyond the rational numbers and consider the real numbers (which include the irrationals—some real numbers are irrational and some are not), we find that the laws of the real numbers have exceeded the bounds of what we can construe in this way. Suppose someone puts the question, "Is the length in inches of this table an irrational number?" Is he asking some kind of question about what result we will get in counting how often a measuring rod must be laid down along the table?

No, we cannot give any such sense to his question. The question has no empirical significance: there is no difference between the answer "Yes" and the answer "No," as regards what they would lead us to expect about the outcome of overt human procedures of counting. However short our measuring rod may be, its use must involve some margin of error, so that counting how often it could be laid down along the table would not settle whether the length is rational or irrational. To determine this, an errorless or an infinitely short rod would be needed. But such rods are impossible, and it makes no real sense to talk about the doing of something that is necessarily impossible. This illustrates how the theory of real numbers, in distinguishing between rational numbers and irrational numbers, has introduced a subtlety which goes beyond the procedure of counting. Here the intricacy of the mathematical formulas has begun to outrun our capacity to construe them as statements about counting: the theorem that a real number is either rational or irrational cannot be viewed as a true statement about counting. The arithmetic of transfinite numbers, and, a fortiori, all forms of set theory in which it is derivable, go still further in this direction, of course. For example, the theorem that there are more real numbers than there are rational numbers cannot be construed as a truth about our procedures of counting. Here the elaboration of the mathematical formulas has far outrun the bounds of what can be construed as statements.

For these parts of mathematics, then, the viewpoint of the formalist is appropriate. Here we have no plausible way of regarding the theorems as true-or-false statements, and we are reduced to viewing these parts of mathematics as games with marks. They are games which can be of great intellectual interest—just as chess is. Moreover, unlike chess, they sometimes do have important applications. Thus, the theory of real numbers is fruitfully used by physicists, and they find it much more profitable to employ than the narrower theory of the rational numbers.

It is likely that one of the hidden motives behind the philosophy of mathematical intuitionism was an obscure feeling that mathematics ought to be limited to formulas which can be interpreted as truths about counting. However, one could accept the view that mathematics ought to be limited in this way, without accepting mathematical intuitionism. A philosophy of mathematics which insists upon this limitation would resemble intuitionism, in that it would insist upon constructive methods of mathematical reasoning. It would not need to be a form of intuitionism, however, for it would not need to embrace conceptualism or the Kantian doctrine of 'pure intuition.' Such a 'finitary' view of mathematics could adopt that which is attractive in mathematical intuitionism, while rejecting its unattractive metaphysics.

Would there be any real justification for the philosophical view that mathematics ought to limit itself to formulas which can be interpreted as truths about counting? Surely the distinction between mathematical theorems that can be construed as expressing truths about counting and those that cannot is philosophically worth emphasizing, and surely it is interesting to investigate how much of classical mathematics can be construed as truths about counting. Yet it would be unreasonably extreme to hold that only the study of theorems of that sort deserves the name of mathematics. The term "mathematics" has come to be established as a name for various kinds of studies, having various sorts of significance: it would have been impertinent and unreasonable if anyone had told Cantor, for instance, that the study he was pursuing is not mathematics. Although some of us may feel a preference for mathematical theorems that can be construed as truths about counting, we should not let this blind us to the utility, interest, and mathematical legitimacy of many theorems that cannot be so construed. The house of mathematics has many mansions, and in it many games are played.

For

further

reading

General

Benacerraf, Paul, and Hilary Putnam, *Philosophy of Mathematics: A Book of Readings*. Englewood Cliffs, N.J.: Prentice-Hall, Inc., 1964.

Chapter 1   Introduction

Hospers, John, *An Introduction to Philosophical Analysis*, Chap. 2. Englewood Cliffs, N.J.: Prentice-Hall, Inc., 1953.

Kant, Immanuel, *Critique of Pure Reason*, Sections I-V of Introduction and Section 1, Chap. 2 of Bk. II of the "Transcendental Analytic."

Waismann, Friedrich, "Verifiability," in *Proceedings of the Aristotelian Society*, Supplementary Vol. 19. Reprinted in *Logic and Language (First Series)*, ed. Anthony Flew. Oxford: Basil Blackwell & Mott, 1955.

Chapter 2   Euclidean Geometry

Euclid, *The Thirteen Books of Euclid's Elements*, ed. Sir Thomas Heath. New York: Dover Publications, Inc., 1956. (Paperback.)

Kant, Immanuel, *Prolegomena to Any Future Metaphysics*, Sections 1-13. New York: Liberal Arts Press, 1950. (Paperback.)

Chapter 3   Non-Euclidean Geometry

Blanché, Robert, *Axiomatics*. New York: The Free Press of Glencoe, 1962. (Paperback.)

Blumenthal, Leonard M., *A Modern View of Geometry*, Chaps. I and III. San Francisco: W. H. Freeman & Co., Pubs., 1961. (Paperback.)

Grünbaum, Adolf, *Philosophical Problems of Space and Time*. New York: Alfred A. Knopf, Inc., 1963.

Hempel, Carl G., "Geometry and Empirical Science," *American Mathematical Monthly*, Vol. 52 (1945). Reprinted in *Readings in Philosophical Analysis*, ed. Herbert Feigl and Wilfred Sellars. New York: Appleton-Century-Crofts, Inc., 1949.

Nagel, Ernest, *The Structure of Science*, Chaps. 8, 9. New York: Harcourt, Brace & World, Inc., 1961.

Poincaré, Henri, *Science and Hypothesis*, Chaps, III, IV, and V. New York: Dover Publications, Inc., 1955. (Paperback.)

Reichenbach, Hans, *The Philosophy of Space and Time*. New York: Dover Publications, Inc., 1958. (Paperback.)

Chapter 4   Numbers and Literalistic Philosophies of Number

Bunge, Mario, *Intuition and Science*, Chap. 2. Englewood Cliffs, N.J.: Prentice-Hall, Inc., 1962. (Paperback.)

Frege, Gottlob, *The Foundations of Arithmetic*, trans. J. L. Austin. Oxford: Basil Blackwell & Mott, 1953.

Quine, W. V., *From a Logical Point of View*, Chap. VI. Cambridge, Mass.: Harvard University Press, 1953.

Russell, Bertrand, *Introduction to Mathematical Philosophy*. London: George Allen & Unwin, 1919.

Stoll, Robert R., *Sets, Logic and Axiomatic Theories*, Chaps. 1, 3. San Francisco: W. H. Freeman & Co., Pubs., 1961. (Paperback.)

Waismann, Friedrich, *Introduction to Mathematical Thinking*. New York: Harper & Row, 1959. (Paperback.)

Chapter 5   Transition to a Nonliteralistic View of Number

Carnap, Rudolf, "Empiricism, Semantics, and Ontology," *Revue internationale de Philosophie*, Vol. 11 (1950). Reprinted in *Semantics and the Philosophy of Language*, ed. Leonard Linsky. Urbana: University of Illinois Press, 1952.

Fränkel, Abraham A., and Yehoshua Bar-Hillel, *Foundations of Set Theory*. Amsterdam: North-Holland Publishing Co., 1958.

Gödel, Kurt, *On Formally Undecidable Propositions of Principia Mathematica and Related Systems*, trans. B. Meltzer. Edinburgh: Oliver & Boyd, 1962.

Hempel, Carl G., "On the Nature of Mathematical Truth," *American Mathematical Monthly*, Vol. 52 (1945). Reprinted in *Readings in Philosophical Analysis*, ed. Herbert Feigl and Wilfred Sellars. New York: Appleton-Century-Crofts, 1949.

Henkin, Leon, "Are Logic and Mathematics Identical?" *Science*, Vol. 138, No. 3542 (November 16, 1962) pp. 788-794.

Mill, John Stuart, *A System of Logic*, Bk. II, Chaps. V and VI.

Nagel, Ernest and James R. Newman, *Gödel's Proof*. New York: New York University Press, 1958. (Paperback.)

Quine, W. V., "Paradox," *Scientific American*, Vol. 206, No. 4 (April, 1962) pp. 84-96.

———, *Set Theory and Its Logic*. Cambridge, Mass.: Harvard University Press, 1963.

Wilder, Raymond L., *Introduction to the Foundations of Mathematics*. New York: John Wiley & Sons, Inc., 1952.

Wittgenstein, Ludwig, *Remarks on the Foundations of Mathematics*. Oxford: Basil Blackwell & Mott, 1956.

INDEX